COMMON BIRDS

COMMON BIRDS

SÁLIM ALI

AND

LAEEQ FUTEHALLY

NATIONAL BOOK TRUST, INDIA

New Delhi

July 1967 (Asadha, 1889)

© Sálim Ali and Laeeq Futehally, 1967

Rs. 15·00

Chief Stockists in India:
INDIA BOOK HOUSE
BOMBAY 1 — CALCUTTA 16 — NEW DELHI 1
MADRAS 2 — BANGALORE 9 — HYDERABAD 29

Distributed in the U.S.A. by

LAWRENCE VERRY INCORPORATED

Mystic, Connecticut 06355

PRINTED IN INDIA
PUBLISHED BY THE SECRETARY, NATIONAL BOOK TRUST, INDIA, NEW DELHI-13
AND PRINTED BY SRI S. N. GUHA RAY AT SREE SARASWATY PRESS LTD.,
32, ACHARYA PRAFULLA CHANDRA ROAD, CALCUTTA-9.

FOREWORD

This is another addition to the Series that the National Book Trust has planned on "India—the Land and People".

The origin of the Series is the result of a discussion that I had with the late Prime Minister, Pandit Jawaharlal Nehru. When I first put the idea before him, he not only heartily approved it but gave many suggestions for making it more complete and attractive. It was his opinion that such a Series of books on India will form a permanent library of knowledge on every aspect of this country and is sure to make constructive contribution for national advancement in knowledge and education.

The Series proposes to cover every aspect of the country and will deal with its geography, geology, botany, zoology, agriculture, anthropology, culture, language, etc. Its ultimate aim is to create a kind of comprehensive library of books on India. We have endeavoured to have the books written by acknowledged authorities on various subjects and in a scientific way. Every effort is being made to see that they are easily understandable by the ordinary educated reader. The factual knowledge regarding the various subjects concerning India would be available to any ordinary reader who is not a specialist and who would like to have a knowledge of the subject in a relatively simple language.

We have been fortunate in getting the guidance of leading experts and scientists in various fields for this Project. In fact without their active cooperation it would not have been possible to plan the Series. We are thankful to our Board of Honorary Editors who are eminent specialists and leaders in their field for helping us in producing these volumes for the benefit of the ordinary reader.

One of the objects of the Series is to make it available in as many Indian languages as practically possible. The work of translating them in various languages will be taken up as soon as the original books are ready. In fact a few volumes might be originally written in some of the languages.

We have received full support from the Ministry of Education of the Government of India and the State Governments. They are lending their help in many ways not the least by permitting scientists working under them to write for the Series. I would like to take this opportunity of thanking them. Without their help it would not have been possible to undertake this enterprise of national utility.

I am very grateful to my colleague, Professor M. S. Thacker, Member of the Planning Commission, for agreeing to be co-Chief Editor. His enthusiastic collaboration has greatly helped in planning the Series successfully.

NEW DELHI   B. V. KESKAR
February 20, 1967

CONTENTS

x   CONTENTS

THE PUBLISHERS ARE GRATEFUL TO THE
BOMBAY NATURAL HISTORY SOCIETY, BOMBAY,
FOR LOANING SOME OF THE BLOCKS OF
THE COLOUR PLATES FOR THIS PUBLICATION.

INTRODUCTION

ALL THE VERTEBRATE or backboned animal life in the world is divided into two classes, the warm-blooded animals and the cold blooded. The former group includes those whose blood keeps a constant temperature and is little affected by the temperature of the surrounding air. The latter group includes fishes, frogs and reptiles whose blood temperature changes with the temperature of the surrounding atmosphere. The warm-blooded animals are further subdivided into Mammals (including human beings), which are covered with hair, bear live young and suckle them, and Birds, which are covered with feathers, lay eggs and as a rule incubate them with the heat of their bodies. It is with the method of classifying this group of avians or birds that we are here concerned.

Birds are easy to define. They are the only feathered creatures in the world. At first sight it might seem that all birds have most characteristics in common since they nearly all fly about, and build nests and lay eggs. A closer look will show that in fact bird life includes many forms which are very different from each other and which sometimes seem to bear very little relationship to each other after all. It includes the tiny humming bird which is not bigger than a man's thumb and the ostrich which stands as high as a pony. It includes birds which can fly thousands of miles, and others like the penguin which cannot raise themselves off the ground. It includes birds which weave elaborate nests like the weaver birds and others which lay their eggs straight on the ground without any preparation. It includes birds which require highly specialized food, others like vultures which feed exclusively on carrion, and still others like crows which will eat practically anything except metal. It includes birds which make two long distance migratory journeys every year, and others who spend their lifetime in the vicinity of one garden. It includes birds like the domestic hen whose chicks start running about and scratching for themselves as soon as they are hatched and others like the parakeets and eagles whose chicks cannot leave their nests for several weeks. And it includes, finally, birds which seem to be unable to live away from the company of man, and others who retreat and become extinct as soon as humans make inroads into their domains. How is such a conglomeration to be reduced to order?

Aristotle made the first attempt to bring some sort of system into the classification of animal life. The next big step was taken by Linnaeus, a Swedish naturalist of the eighteenth century whose system, with some modifications, is universally being used today.

All bird life, then, is divided into 27 main Orders, based on fundamental differences of structure and development. The order Passeriformes, for instance, includes most of those birds which live in trees and with which we are likely to be most familiar. The order Ciconiiformes includes all the storks and herons who spend their lives near the water, while the order Anseriformes consists of the swimming birds like ducks, geese and swans.

The broad category of Orders is again divided into Families. The family is a group of birds which share some strong characteristics. The order Passeriformes or Perching Birds, for instance, includes about 40 families among them the flycatchers (Muscicapidae) the crows (Corvidae) and the sunbirds (Nectariniidae). The families are almost literally families, for they consist of species which are close to each other in the evolutionary hierarchy and share an obvious resemblance in behaviour and habits. The habits are reflected in the shape of the beaks and claws, sometimes even the wings, and the general shape and movements of the birds. The effect of feeding habits on claws and beaks will be dealt with in detail later on. Often it is possible to place a new or unfamiliar bird within its family even if the exact species is unknown. The strong hooked beak of a hawk with the upper mandible curving over the lower, the flat head, fierce eye and powerful build are unmistakable. One may not know the exact species to which an individual belongs but it is comparatively simple to guess whether it belongs to the hawk family or not. In the same way, sunbirds have very thin long slightly curved bills with which they probe into the tubes or corollas of flowers for nectar. The bill and the general shape and behaviour of the bird is enough to enable an observer to place it within its family. Sometimes of course these superficial resemblances may be deceptive, merely brought about by similar feeding habits. For example, parakeets and hawks both possess hooked bills but belong to entirely different families and even orders. Similarly the humming birds of the New World are entirely different from the sunbirds of the Old World though in outward appearance and flower-probing habits they are almost identical.

The group which comes next below the Family is the Genus, a unit much smaller than the family, which includes a number of closely related species. The genus is entirely man-made for convenience in grouping together a number of species possessing similar characteristics. Linnaeus laid great stress on the genus, although it is now considered less important than it used to be. There has always been, and continues to be, room for differences of opinion among experts about the placing of species within the genera. The main importance of the genus for us at present is that it is the genus which provides the first part of the scientific name of each species. All the members of the same genus have a common surname. Thus there are several different species of crows possessing certain common features, and they are all grouped under the same genus— *Corvus*.

The final division in the classifying of birds is the splitting of the genera into species. The Species is a recognizable natural unit. The test for inclusion in a species is inter-breeding. A species includes similar individual birds which are capable of breeding with each other and reproducing their own kind. In this way all the red-vented bulbuls, in spite of minor differences, belong to one species, the redwhiskered bulbuls belong to another species and the white-cheeked bulbuls belong to a third species, and so on. There are often slight variations in size and shade of coloration in the plumage within the species because of climate and the geographical conditions of the environment. Those that live in northern areas are normally larger than their southern counterparts; those that live in moist climates tend to have darker colours than members of the same species which live in drier climates, and so on. Where such differences are fairly marked and consistent, the species is further split by taxonomists into Races or Subspecies. But the different races are capable of inter-breeding and remain within the species, which is always the final unit in classification.

Every bird then can be placed first within its order, then in its family which is narrowed down to its genus, and last of all it can be exactly described by being placed in its species and often geographical race. There are altogether about 8650 species of living birds in the world today. The 27 orders, under which they are arranged in a 'natural' sequence, begin with the one which is believed to be the least highly developed like the grebes and divers and end with the Passeriformes (or perching birds) which is considered to be the most highly advanced. There is, however, some difference of opinion about the developmental hierarchy within this order, thus some authorities placing the crows at the top, others the finches.

We have in India today about 1200 species of birds representing some 75 families and 20 orders. This is a very high number and represents a great variety for a single country. The reason for this is that we can boast of a great variety of climates, from moist tropical to the cold arctic of the Himalayan ranges, the dry hot desert climate of Rajasthan and the cool temperate climate of the hilly portions. We can provide dense jungles, light forests, open country, cultivated agricultural areas, the sea coast, river beds, rocky cliffs and high mountains. We can provide different types of ecological habitats to please the taste of hundreds of species. The birds we see in India are a splendid cross-section of the total bird population of the world. Many species are resident throughout the year, while others come here as migrants to spend the winter months. The birds which are conspicuously absent from our shores are of the orders and families which belong entirely or chiefly to the New World and Australia, and others like the penguins which belong to the cold Antarctic seas.

ORNITHOLOGY AND BIRDWATCHING

BIRD STUDY as we know it today was virtually non-existent in India before the advent of the British. Although a good deal of rather random collecting and classifying of birds had been done since the early years of the 19th century—chiefly by British civil and military personnel in the service of the East India Company—Indian ornithology proper may be said to date only from the publication in 1862-64 of *The Birds of India* by T. C. Jerdon. Dr. Jerdon was an army surgeon who had spent many years of his service in various parts of the country and collected and studied birds assiduously. The book collated all the information gathered by himself and previous observers, two of the most famous of these veterans being Brian Hodgson and Edward Blyth. The former was the British Resident in Nepal and the latter had come out to India as curator of the Asiatic Society's museum in Calcutta. Before Jerdon (and even after and until recently) the principal activity of ornithologists in India consisted of shooting and collecting birds for classification, often vicariously with the help of local shikaris and trappers. This was important at the time as many of the birds were still unknown and had to be studied in the museum, described, and named. Popular interest in birdwatching had not yet developed, and the poor quality of field glasses and lack of simple illustrated bird books made identification difficult unless the bird was in hand. In those days, moreover, museum zoologists were inclined to look down on birdwatching as merely a childish way of killing time indulged in by the idle rich, and devoid of any real scientific value. Thus shooting specimens and collecting eggs remained for a long time the chief 'respectable' activity of ornithologists in India. Jerdon's *Birds of India* introduced a refreshing element of novelty. Besides describing the superficial structure and plumage of the various species, it also furnished short readable accounts of their general habits, of interest to the layman. The book gave an immediate fillip to the activities of bird lovers, or 'watchers', and registered a marked widening of the circle of enthusiastic 'amateur' field naturalists.

The second significant advance in the study of Indian birds was brought about by that remarkable man Allan Octavian Hume—a Britisher in the civil service—who, besides being a giant among ornithologists is memorable also as being one of the founders of the Indian National Congress. For many years Hume dominated the field, and by his energy and infectious dynamism rallied round himself an active band of sportsmen-naturalists scattered over all parts of the country, whom he encouraged and guided in collecting skins and keeping field notes in a meaningful way. He identified and reported on their specimens, describing many new species in the process; he edited their notes and published them in the journal for Indian ornithology *Stray Feathers*, which he had founded. The eleven volumes of *Stray Feathers* published between 1872-1888 have added to our knowledge basically, and no serious work on Indian birds is possible without constant delving into their contents.

Lay interest in Indian birds and their habits received a further boost by the appearance between 1889 and 1898 of the four volumes on birds in the India Office sponsored *Fauna of British India* series, by E. W. Oates and W. T. Blanford. Both the authors were expert ornithologists yet 'amateur' in the sense that the former was a Public Works Department engineer and the latter a government geologist. These volumes took count of all the additional information that had accumulated through the labours of Hume and his band of disciples; it brought classification and scientific nomenclature in line with the modernised notions then current, and—what is more—it brought within its ambit Sind, Kashmir, Assam, Bengal (including the present East Pakistan), Burma, Andaman and Nicobar Islands, and Ceylon, which had remained largely ornithologically unexplored in Jerdon's day. Thus the first edition of what is familiarly known to bird students as *The Fauna* covered the entire British Indian Empire as it then was, and vastly enlarged the 'catchment area' for field studies and notes. Bird lovers everywhere—mostly British planters and civil and military officials—were quick to take advantage of the guidance it provided, and *The Fauna* accelerated the pace of Indian bird study tremendously. After *Stray Feathers* had ceased publication, notes and regional papers on Indian birds had begun to appear increasingly in the then newly started *Journal of the Bombay Natural History Society*. Ever since that time the *Journal* (now in its 63rd volume) has continued to function as the main repository of writings on Indian birds contributed by an expanding circle of able field naturalists from all walks of life.

Thus by the end of the 1920s with the significant increase in the knowledge of geographical distributions and habits, the need for a revision of *The Fauna* was seriously felt. The second edition, which ran into eight volumes in place of the previous four, was completed between 1921 and 1930 also by another expert 'amateur' E. C. Stuart Baker—an officer of the Indian Police who had spent his service in Assam and collected and studied birds and their nesting habits intensively. The *New Fauna* not only brought up-to-date the classification, nomenclature, and general information concerning Indian birds but was a definite advance on its predecessors in the purposiveness and scientific quality of its contents, more in keeping with the current trends and progress of ornithology in western countries. It pointed clearly to the gaps in our knowledge of Indian birds, and indicated where further work was necessary, thus posing a challenge that bird students were not slow to take up.

During the 35 years since the publication of the *New Fauna* a considerable amount of collecting and field study was done in various little-explored parts of the subcontinent, still largely by Britishers but with an increasing Indian contribution, more especially since our independence in 1947. The two names that stand out among workers of that period are Hugh Whistler and Claude B. Ticehurst. The former, like Stuart Baker, was an officer of the Indian Police; the latter a medical doctor whose special interest in Indian birds began during World War I when he was posted in various parts of what is now West Pakistan with the Royal Army Medical Corps. Both these workers contributed significantly to Indian ornithology before and particularly since the publication of the *New Fauna*. The stage has now been reached when there is no longer any need for collecting bird skins in India except of special groups or in remote unexplored pockets. We have enough material available for taxonomic study in the great museums of the world which can be readily loaned for research. The greatest need now is to turn from the museum and laboratory to the field—in other words to pursue the study of the living bird in its natural habitat and collect precise information about its ecology, habits, and behaviour: how and where the bird lives, how it is adapted to its environment, how it acquires a mate, what sort of nest it makes and how it brings up its family, its social organization and its population dynamics. From the economic point of view it is important to investigate the food and feeding habits of birds and assess their status as friends or foes of man. In an agricultural, forested and thickly populated country like ours, constantly faced with food shortages, this is a matter of particular significance and urgency. All this information cannot be obtained from dry museum skins.

Discovering the life-histories of different species, and the manner in which these mesh in with other forms of life is extremely slow and requires great patience and perseverance. The life-histories of only a very few species have so far been studied in India and that rather superficially. Our knowledge about the habits and behaviour of most birds is still elementary and scattered. Pertinent and reliable information supplied by amateur birdwatchers may sometimes prove of great value in piecing together the life story of a species.

The first step in birdwatching is the ability to recognize, with confidence, the common birds of any locality. Unless one is able to do this, it is impossible to go any further, just as it is impossible to read without knowing the alphabet. In order to acquire the ABC of birdwatching, it is necessary to possess three items of equipment: a pair of binoculars, a notebook and a reference book for identification.

The most suitable size of binoculars for birdwatching is 8×30 or 7×50. It is important that they should not be too bulky to carry about, and that they should, at the same time, give an adequate magnification and be capable of focussing at fairly close range. To begin with, the aspiring birdwatcher will have to identify the birds which he sees in the field with the help of books. It is hoped that the present volume will be of some help; the other two most useful books are Whistler's *Popular Handbook of Indian Birds*, and Sálim Ali's *The Book of Indian Birds*. The latter contains charts listing birds according to their sizes, chief colours and most obvious features, (*e.g.* long bills, legs, etc.) together with coloured illustrations of each species, which makes identification comparatively simple.

In order to identify a bird, it is above all necessary to ensure oneself of just *what* one has seen. For instance, one might see a small black and white bird. It is important to be sure exactly which parts of the body were white—whether the white was on the head, in the tail, or underparts. It is also important to notice one or two other features of the bird, the shape and colour of the bill, size and colour of the legs and tail, and any other special feature like a crest. Since it is unlikely that one would be able to notice so many things at the first time of seeing a bird—which may be a very brief glimpse as it flits among the foliage—it is better to concentrate on memorizing one or two definite facts rather than attempt to take in too many impressions. In other words, it is easier to identify a bird if one knows that it was the size of a myna and had red legs rather than if one knew that it was brown and red with a bit of black and grey. Another fact which adds to the complications of identification is that our memories are far less reliable than we like to think. It is not only probable but almost certain, that we shall forget the colouring and other points about the bird we have seen in a couple of hours. It is imperative therefore to write down at once what we have seen, and it is in order to do this that we need to carry our third piece of equipment, the notebook and pencil, always on our person.

Ideally, on the few occasions that one gets a grand-stand view of a bird for a long time, one should put down everything about it. This would include its size (compared with some familiar bird), general colour, any special markings and their positions, the size, shape and colour of the bill, legs, wings, tail, neck, and if possible eyes. A sketch made on the spot, howsoever rough and ready, usually helps. It is also important to note where the bird was seen—on the ground, or among leaves, on a stump, or on the water, etc. and its actions at the time. Some birds have definite or characteristic modes of action like hopping, or a special way of flying, which make their identification easy, and this should certainly be noted. The call or song of birds is another useful identification mark, but often this is difficult to describe in words. Still, even a slight hint at the sort of sound it makes (*e.g.* a single note, whistle or clicking sound made in flight, or sharp chirrup) can be a useful guide to its identity. The date and the type of habitat in which the bird was seen are, of course, all-important. Some dates may rule out certain migrants or help to explain unfamiliar breeding plumage, while a good description of the habitat can often narrow down the field of possibles to manageable limits.

Although books and pictures describe a bird's colouring in detail, the newcomer to birdwatching will soon discover that it is very unlikely that he will be able to see all the colours and markings clearly the first time. This is particularly true in the case of birds seen on the wing, and also of tree-haunting species which are usually seen between the light and shade of foliage. Even open sunlight can be surprisingly deceptive, and colours seen from certain angles, especially with the naked eyes, are apt to look very different from what they are in fact. It is therefore important not to rely for identification simply on a bird's colouring, but to note at least one other feature like the bill, legs, crest, or tail.

After a little practice it will be found that it is often possible to place even unknown birds within their families—family looks and family habits give them away, as in the case of human families. The flight of the egret family with neck folded back, the kingfishers' bill, the head and beak of the hawks, to mention only a few characteristics, make the birds which possess them recognizable as members of a certain family even when it is not possible to pin down the exact species. Another identifying mark which becomes more and more useful with practice is *movement*. Certain species, and sometimes several related species, have similar movements which conform to a pattern. All the flycatchers, for instance make the same kind of sallies after little flying insects, and it is often possible to recognize a flycatcher even without seeing it clearly simply because it flies in a certain manner, or to know a wren-warbler by its twitching flight. For the advanced birdwatcher, the identification of rare or vagrant species is usually possible by reference to the collection of specimens at the Bombay Natural History Society, or at the Zoological Survey of India in Calcutta.

The discovery of a nest where it can be watched fairly easily is of course a great boon, and it provides a wonderful chance to become familiar with the bird in question. It is important to watch the nest with extreme caution in order not to give away its whereabouts to crows or other predators, while at the same time one should resist the temptation to handle the eggs or chicks. It is not true that parents will refuse to feed a chick which has been handled by man, but young chicks are extremely delicate and should not be touched or frightened. In those unusual circumstances when it becomes absolutely necessary to handle a bird, as for instance in the case of an injured bird, the bird should be held correctly; lightly but firmly pinning its wings to its side in the palm of the hand, with the first and middle finger on either side of its neck. Some of the smaller birds are extremely frail, and even a slight pressure on the chest may be fatal. A good way when examining a bird is to put it on its back in the palm of the hand, as it has a tendency to lie completely still as long as it is on its back. It should be released by turning it round in the grip described above and launched.

It is not possible for every birdwatcher to make new or startling discoveries about birds. But the intimacy which is built up by carefully watching and studying birds over a long time will remain a source of delight and provide a lifelong hobby which can be practised under almost any conditions.

REPRODUCTION

FOR ALL BIRDS, bringing up a family successfully is the most anxious business of the year, fraught with hazards and dangers which are of course increased when a long migratory journey precedes the nest-building. A nesting bird family is in an extremely vulnerable position and it needs every kind of help and protection from its environment. The birds need cover in which to hide the nest; they need building material; they need warm weather, first for the protection of their eggs and later their chicks; they need a plentiful supply of food for the chicks and lastly they need long daylight hours in which to search for the food. On the whole the most important item is the food supply. Birds will choose a nesting season when they can be sure of a liberal supply of food even if it is a little inconvenient in other ways. This is illustrated by the smaller birds which nest in the Bombay neighbourhood during the monsoon. It seems amazing that they should choose to build their frail nests at a time when they are in constant danger from the lashing winds and rain. But the insects and worms which make their appearance at this time, all ready to be eaten, more than outweigh the danger of being washed away. In the colder countries, of course, the breeding period for nearly all birds is during spring and summer when conditions are most favourable. It has been noticed even here that the slightly different nesting times of the different species is dependent on the slightly different seasons when their favourite caterpillar or worm is most plentiful.

Each species, then, breeds in just that season when it can be assured of an optimum food supply and when the surrounding conditions are least inimical. The physiological readiness for breeding seems to be geared to the right season. Many birds are known not to breed at all when weather conditions are not to their liking. The flamingo which breeds in the Rann of Kutch after the monsoon is very particular about waiting for the right conditions. In some years when the rainfall has been too heavy or too slight, it refuses to nest at all.

As their breeding season approaches, the males put on their breeding plumage. This may be a fine lot of new feathers, or an extra patch of colour, as in the case of the cattle egret which acquires an orange tinge on the head and neck, or it may simply be that the existing feathers are renovated to give the owner a sprucer look. At the same time most males also acquire a song or at least, add a few extra sounds to their workaday calls. Song is not to be confused with the usual call notes which are used during the rest of the year chiefly for maintaining contact between individuals. The special song which is developed at this time is a definite instrument to be used in the business of breeding. It has been found that some of the most beautiful songsters have been given their voice for a serious purpose, *i.e.* in order to assert their possession and warn rivals to keep away from their nesting territory, whereas it used to be thought that the main purpose of bird song was to attract a female. While it is not known whether the quality of a male's singing can influence her choice of a mate, it is true that the song advertises the presence of an unattached male who has marked' out a territory for himself and is only waiting for the right mate in order to start building a nest. Because of the limited availability of food in any given area, the smaller songbirds know that more than one family could not be raised within that area. The males, therefore, select a certain territory, and fight off any other males who intrude into it. The loud song is the most powerful weapon in their armoury. In the breeding season, even those birds which cannot sing in any manner, develop some kind of an extra noisiness: thus the storks which have no vocal muscles, manage to make a clattering noise with their mandibles.

Most birds have some kind of courtship display when the male seeks to win the female's heart and hand. The peacock's dance is well known, and he uses it indiscriminately to impress anyone, whether bird or man, who happens to be looking on, and often even when no one is looking! The roller tumbles and turns somersaults in the air in a series of clever antics before a watching female, while parakeets posture and pose ludicrously, standing first on one foot then the other. Some male birds simply keep showing off their special brilliant plumage to the female in a flamboyant series of posturing and strutting, while some conduct their courtship in a quiet discreet manner. With some birds, as in the case of the bayas, the act of building a nest is itself a form of courtship and the female chooses as mate the bird whose nest happens to catch her fancy. In many species the offering of a worm or some other titbit is a part of the courtship, and the female often takes full advantage of the male's ardent mood to beg for delicacies from him.

The next stage is for the pair, or in some cases only the male or the female of the pair, to set about building a nest. As a general rule, birds build their nests in the sort of surroundings in which they are accustomed to live. An eagle, accustomed to living at great heights will build on high exposed cliff-faces and rocks. Arboreal birds will build among the leaves of trees; birds which spend much of their time on the ground like partridges and quails lay their eggs on the ground; birds which live on the water like cormorants and herons will build near the water, and so forth. This is the general pattern but within it there is room for innumerable exceptions. To mention only two, the bee-eater which is by no means a ground bird builds a horizontal tunnel in earth banks, and many ducks make their nests in trees.

In the shape and structure of the nests themselves there is tremendous diversity. Some of the ground birds simply scrape a little earth to one side and lay their eggs in the depression; at the other extreme is the well-known, compactly woven baya's nest which is an elaborate affair with an inner egg chamber, as carefully worked as if it were made by the hands of an expert basket weaver. Some birds nest in an old hole in a decayed branch or wall which they line with soft materials, some dig tunnels, and some build cups of grasses in branches. Some water birds like the jaçanas build their skimpy nest on the floating leaves of water plants. Some birds, as we have already said, like to make sure that no other birds of the same species will build in the vicinity, while others nest in large colonies. There is, of course, safety in numbers, but strangely enough it is often the larger and less vulnerable birds like the storks, herons and egrets which build in colonies while the small and gentle passerines like the tailor birds, wren-warblers, and robins build singly and rely on camouflage. One possible explanation is that the smaller birds are unable to cover long distances in search of food and need to be assured that there will be no rival for the food supply nearby. The bigger birds on the other hand are far-ranging and can look for food farther afield so that the presence of a rival food hunter is not important for them.

The work of incubation and feeding the young is divided in different proportions between the partners in the different species. In some cases the work is shared equally, in some cases the female takes on the major part of it, while in a few exceptional cases like the painted snipe and the jaçana the male does most of the domestic work by himself. In every case, though, the parents of young chicks have to work extremely hard. It is estimated that in the first few days a young chick eats twice its own weight in food every day. The rate of growth of the nestlings is phenomenal, but it is only in the early stages that they have to be fed at this pace. For the first week or so after the eggs hatch, although the parents are harried from sun-up until sun-down, ceaselessly making foraging trips, the brood is never satisfied.

Even when the chicks escape from predators and other accidents, life in the nest may be full of risk. A chick which hatches after all the rest, or which is weak from the beginning, may find that its siblings get all the food, for it is always the more insistently demanding beaks which are filled first. There is also the danger of a weakling being trampled in the nest or falling out. These are dangers in addition to the outside dangers from cats, lizards, rats, snakes, crows and other birds, storms, wind, and other natural hazards which do not end even on the chick leaving the nest. This explains why, although many species raise more than one brood successively and lay several eggs in each clutch, they barely succeed in reproducing themselves and maintaining the level of the population. Naturally, the more vulnerable species lay larger clutches, like the ducks, or raise more than one brood each season, like the smaller songbirds. If a nestful of chicks or eggs is destroyed, the parents waste no time in mourning. They start work on a new nest at once. As we said at the beginning of this chapter, the urge to reproduce themselves is the strongest instinct among birds, as it is in all animals, and they will overcome surprising obstacles to do so.

MIGRATION

THE MIGRATION OF BIRDS is one of the strangest of all ornithological phenomena as well as its unsolved mystery. Twice every year, in Spring and Autumn, millions of birds take to the air and set out on long journeys in order to get to a definite goal, sometimes across oceans and continents. What compels them to go? Why do they face the dangers of such a hazardous journey? And how do they know which route to take? These basic questions have not yet been satis- factorily answered although careful experiments and large scale ringing of migrants have now given us a knowledge of many more *facts* than we ever had before.

The quality which defines all bird migration is the regularity of the back and forth swing between two end localities. The movements are predictable to about within a week, sometimes even closer. The birds return to the same areas—often to the same garden or field— in both their summer and winter homes, which may be separated by as much as several thousand miles.

The question which first comes to mind is, why do some species of birds migrate and not others? The obvious answer is that migra- tion has a survival value for some species and not for others. In some species the survival value must be marginal because some of their members stay at home while others migrate. Examples of the un- decided species are our coots and spoonbills. A part of their popula- tion migrates every year, while others remain within the country without suffering any apparent disadvantage.

In the northern hemisphere the autumn migration from the breeding grounds moves from north to south and from the higher altitudes to the lower. In the southern hemisphere the directions are reversed, naturally, with the birds travelling northwards to escape the southern winter. It is understandable that many birds should prefer to avoid a harsh winter and leave for a milder climate before it overtakes them, and that they should return to their homeland as it begins to get warm. The birds arrive at the latter at a time when all the trees are budding with leaf and flower and there are plenty of worms and insects on which to feed a family. By the end of the summer the chicks are grown and independent, and before the first autumn coolness starts to be felt the birds are ready for the southward journey. Some birds seem to spend only the minimal time in their breeding grounds. The Rosy Pastor, for instance which breeds in central Asia, leaves India in May and is generally back again in August. Most birds, however, take a little longer: they leave us in March and return in September.

Thus far, the arduous migratory journeys seem to have a certain value, perhaps even a certain necessity, for the birds that undertake them. But what is puzzling is that there are certain East-West migrations as well, when the birds move to another place on roughly the same latitude with a similar climate, for nesting. Then again, many birds make short journeys of a few miles only and it is difficult to see how these local migrations can be so vitally necessary or even beneficial. In Bombay for instance, birds like the orioles and the bee-eaters leave the city areas and go a short distance inland to the Deccan Plateau or central India during the monsoon, returning punctually in early September. Beyond the fact that these local migrations do take place on a fairly large scale, we do not know very much about them yet, for until we can ring birds in sufficiently large numbers we shall not be able to collect accurate data about their movements.

Another factor which adds complexity to the whole picture of migration is that, while for most birds migration is a simple trip to their breeding grounds and back, even when they choose to return by a different route, there are some adventurous individuals which make a much more complicated journey. They go to their breeding grounds, and after finishing the business of raising a family, they go on to another place as if for a holiday. Their return to the winter quarters is again broken by a short stop in their breeding grounds. Bird migration, then, is an extremely intricate series of movements, some of them incomprehensible, whose main characteristics are, as we have said before, their back and forth nature and their regularity, and their main purpose to find the most desirable living conditions for different times of the year.

2

For days before the take-off for the long journey, the migrants are preparing for it. They eat greedily to put on an extra layer of fat which will sustain them during the trip; some even practise forming and flying in flocks or 'balling up' as it is called. Experiments suggest that it is the timing of the rising and setting sun which gives migrants their final cue for departure. The sun is also their compass on their long journeys, for it is now believed that the birds take their orientation from the angle of the sun. Fogs and mists which obscure the sun can throw the birds off their course for a while although with the return of visibility they are able to re-align themselves fairly well. Landmarks, where they exist, are not ignored but the real guide is the sun by day and the stars by night. As the birds usually fly at a height of between 600 and 1300 metres the smaller landmarks would be invisible anyhow, but the most amazing proof of the small importance of landmarks is that in many species the young birds, making the journey for the first time, generally migrate in advance independently of their parents. We are forced to admit that the sense which enables them to steer by the sun is unanalysable and must therefore be called instinct.

A few species always travel singly, although most birds prefer to travel in large or small flocks. Many small birds, otherwise diurnal, prefer to fly by night—perhaps for greater safety from predators. The cruising speed of the smaller birds is round about 30 km. per hour, and as the working day of a migrating bird is calculated to be about eight hours, one lap of the journey should be just under 250 km. Bigger birds can often fly steadily at 80 km. p. h. and consequently cover much longer distances in a day. In crossing seas the birds naturally have to do forced marches and at such times many flocks have been known to fly for anything up to 36 hours without stopping. Frequently a flock may fly into bad weather and high winds, specially when the birds descend for landing, and then the casualties are likely to be very heavy. All in all, a migratory journey is always taxing and arduous and can often be dangerous as well.

The scale of the migratory movements is difficult to imagine. It is estimated that of the species which breed in Europe and the northern part of Asia about 40 per cent. are migrants, that is just less than half. Of the 68 species of songbirds in Britain 22 species are migrants, and of the 1200 species of all kinds found in India over 300 come from distant lands in winter. In another sense, too, the scale of the journeys is astonishing. The Arctic Tern flies from the North Pole to the South Pole and back every year—a round trip of some 35,000 km. It is not unusual for birds to make a journey of several thousand kilometres: many of the species which breed in Europe go as far as S. Africa for the winter; it is also true that a great number simply make a dash for the Mediterranean countries and stay there.

For most of our migrants, India is the winter or the non-breeding end of their migration. Many species which nest in eastern Europe, or northern and central Asia, or even in the Himalayan ranges, come into the Peninsula for winter. Perhaps our most abundant migrants are those that gather on our sea shores and around our rivers and lakes, the ducks and wading birds.

Beyond these bare facts we know exceedingly little about bird migration in India—the exact localities and populations from which the different species are derived, the routes they follow on their journeys to and from the country, and other details connected with the seasonal movements. A method that has been increasingly used throughout the world since the beginning of this century in order to obtain precise information concerning migratory birds is to mark them with aluminium rings round their legs. The birds are netted or trapped, ringed, registered, and then released. The rings are of various appropriate sizes. On them is stamped a serial number and the address of the ringer who should be intimated upon the recovery of the bird, accidentally or in any other way. The Bombay Natural History Society is operating a project for the large scale ringing of various species of migratory birds in different parts of India and has obtained, in the course of the last 5 years, a good deal of factual data that were quite unknown previously. Some of our wild ducks have been recovered over 4800 km. away in Siberia, and many useful bits of information are accumulating from the distant recoveries of other species as well. The rings bear a serial number in addition to the legend "Inform Bombay Nat. Hist. Society". Readers are requested to publicise this fact as widely as possible so that finders may know what to do if they chance to find a ring on a dead bird, and none of the valuable information gets lost. Many birds with foreign rings are also recovered in India. All rings, whether Indian or foreign, should preferably be forwarded to the Society, or if that is not possible, a correct reading of the number, and the circumstances, date and locality where they were found. A proper knowledge of the movements of birds in India can only be built up by cooperative effort of this kind.

DESCRIPTION OF THE BIRDS

The Order PODICIPEDIFORMES—Grebes—contains short-winged almost tailless water birds with the legs placed far back and the toes lobed with a fringe of skin on either side, like a leaf with mid-rid. The most familiar representative of this order within our limits is the **Little Grebe** or **Dabchick** (*Podiceps ruficollis*)—PLATE 1—Hindi: *Pāndūbi, Dūbdūbi,* and *Lāokri*. It is a drab-coloured plump little swimming bird with silky underparts, short pointed bill, and no tail. In breeding plumage the head and neck become dark brown and chestnut and the swollen yellow gape conspicuous. It is seen on practically every pond, village tank and jheel swimming about like a miniature duck and diving on the least suspicion. The birds keep in twos and threes on the smaller tanks, but congregations of 50 and more are not uncommon on the larger jheels. They are past masters in the art of diving, and the rapidity with which a dabchick will disappear beneath the surface leaving scarcely a ripple behind is truly astonishing. When fired at with a shotgun the bird has often vanished before the charge can reach it! They are loth to leave the water, and when disturbed will patter a short distance along the surface and flop down again. However, in spite of their diminutive wings the birds can fly strongly, as when shifting from one tank to another when the water dries, often over considerable distances. The normal call notes are a shrill musical tittering uttered as the birds are disporting themselves of an evening, as is their wont, pattering along the surface, half running half flying, with rapid vibrations of their stumpy wings, chasing one another. Their food consists of aquatic insects and larvae, tadpoles, snails, and tiny fish picked off or from under the floating vegetation, or captured by diving and underwater pursuit. The dabchick's nest is a pad of sodden weed-stems placed on partly submerged floating plants. The eggs—3 to 5—are white when laid but soon become dirty and discoloured through contact with the sodden grasses with which the bird covers them up each time it leaves the nest on disturbance or for feeding. The diminutive downy chicks are striped, and often carried about riding on the parent's back.

The Order **PELECANIFORMES** is represented chiefly by the families PELECANIDAE (pelicans and darters) and PHALACROCORACIDAE (cormorants).

Pelicans are large heavy-looking birds with short stout legs, fully webbed feet and enormous flattened bills underhung by a capacious elastic skin pouch. This is used in the manner of a landing net for catching fish which forms their staple food. In spite of their cumbrous appearance pelicans are remarkably light-boned birds and capable of strong buoyant flight. In common with many of their relations, and with vultures and storks, they spend much of their time soaring on thermal currents and sailing around on motionless wings high up in the heavens on a sunny day. Of the 3 kinds found in India the **Spottedbilled** or **Grey Pelican** (*Pelecanus philippensis*)— PLATE 2—Hindi: *Hăwăsil* or *Kūrēr* is the only resident, the other two normally being winter visitors. In this species the upper mandible is marked with large blue-black spots while the bill-pouch is dull purplish. Adults are greyish white; young birds browner. The blackish wing-quills, conspicuous in flight, and grey-brown tail are further aids to its identification. It is found in small parties or large flocks at jheels, either swimming about fishing, resting buoyantly on the water, or preening themselves on the shore while working up an appetite. They are voracious eaters and devour large quantities of fish. Their hunting, like the cormorants', is a cooperative undertaking, but they do not dive after the quarry. Several birds swim in a semi-circle driving a shoal of fish into the shallows with a vigorous splashing of their great wings. The birds swim into the hemmed-in shoal with open bills and scoop the fish into the expanded pouch. Pelicans rise off the water with little effort and fly with the neck pulled back into a flattened S. The steady wing beats produce a whistling sound and the flat-keeled body is reminiscent of the floats of a flying boat. The Grey Pelican breeds in the East Godavari district of Andhra, and in small numbers also elsewhere in the Peninsula. It nests in large colonies covering extensive areas, in tall leafy trees and palms. The nests are large untidy stick platforms, often several together in the same tree and touching one another. The eggs—normally 3—are chalky white, becoming a dirty brownish as incubation proceeds.

The family PHALACROCORACIDAE includes the Darter or Snake-bird and the Cormorants. The **Darter** (*Anhinga rufa*)—PLATE 3—Hindi: *Bănbé*, is a black water bird with slender snake-like velvety brown neck, narrow head, and pointed dagger bill. Silvery grey streaks on the back and long, stiff, rounded tail are other pointers to its identification. It is seen singly or in small loose parties in and about jheels, village tanks, reservoirs and rivers; sometimes also at tidal estuaries. On the surface the bird swims with the body partially—sometimes completely—submerged leaving only the snake-like head and neck exposed, swaying and turning this way and that. Its staple food is fish. It is an expert diver and submarine swimmer, diving and chasing them under water with wings held half open and head and neck swaying back and forth like a javelin thrower poising his missile. A special contrivance in the neck vertebrae enables the bill to be shot out with lightning rapidity as if released by a powerful spring, transfixing the fish on the stiletto-like lower mandible. The snaky neck now comes above the surface and with a smart upward jerk, the victim is shaken off into the air to be caught between the mandibles and swallowed head foremost. In spite of the narrow head and throat, fishes of amazingly large size are sometimes managed in this way. When sated, the bird perches upright on the top of some tree or stake with wings and tail spread out to dry. For although it spends its life mostly in the water its plumage, strangely enough, is not so waterproof as the duck's. It becomes permeated and bedraggled and needs constant drying out to maintain its efficiency. The usual call notes of the darter are rather metallic disyllabic croaks, *chi-gi, chi-gi,* etc. In flight and general behaviour it resembles the cormorants with which it commonly associates. Darters usually nest in mixed colonies with egrets, storks and such-like birds. The nest is an untidy stick platform built in a tree standing in or near water. The eggs — 3 or 4 — are narrow and long, pale greenish blue with a whitish chalky coating.

The **Little Cormorant** (*Phalacrocorax niger*) — PLATE 4 — Hindi: *Pān kowwa* or *Chhōta gănhil* is slightly larger than the Jungle Crow. It is a shabby looking glistening black duck-like water bird with a longish stiff tail and slender compressed bill, sharply hooked at the tip. There is a small white patch on the throat and a suggestion of a crest on the back of the head.

It is usually found singly, in small flocks, or large close-knit congregations, on village tanks, jheels, and large inland waters; sparingly also on brackish lagoons and tidal creeks. The birds perch on rocks or fishing stakes, or trees overhanging water, sunning themselves with outspread wings. Their food consists mainly of fish. They are accomplished swimmers and divers and all their fishing is done under water. Sometimes they hunt by concerted action, a flock hemming in a school of fish and chasing and diving repeatedly after the quarry, jostling and leap frogging over one another in feverish excitement. The birds come up with their victims held crosswise in the bill, and with a smart upward jerk shift them into position for being swallowed head foremost. They immediately dive again for the next victim, and so on. Astonishingly large fish are sometimes dealt with in this way, and cormorants have seemingly insatiable appetites. Two other species of black cormorant are also commonly found in association with the Little: the **Large Cormorant** (*P. carbo*) and the **Indian Shag** (*P. fuscicollis*). The former is as large as a domestic duck with greyish white on the head and neck in the breeding season and a large oval white patch on the thighs, particularly conspicuous in flight. The Shag is intermediate in size and easily confused with either except in the breeding season when it has tufts of white feathers behind the eyes and some white speckles on the head and neck. All the cormorants build shallow twig platform nests in trees standing in or near water, frequently in mixed colonies with egrets and storks. Their eggs—4 or 5—are pale bluish green with a chalky surface and differ from one another's only in size.

The Order CICONIIFORMES is well represented in India by four families, *viz.* ARDEIDAE (herons, egrets, etc.), CICONIIDAE (storks), THRESKIORNITHIDAE (ibises), and PHOENICOPTERIDAE (flamingos).

Herons and egrets are long-legged birds with partially bare tibia and longish unwebbed toes. They have long and thin flexible necks and pointed spear-like bills. A typical example is the **Grey Heron** (*Ardea cinerea*)— PLATE 5— Hindi: *Nāri, Kābūd, Ănjăn*, a lanky, bare-legged stork-like marsh bird, ashy grey above with white crown and neck; greyish white below. It has a long slender S-shaped neck, narrow head, and stout, pointed, dagger bill. The long black occipital crest, elongated black-streaked white plumes on the breast, and a conspicuous black-dotted line down the middle of the foreneck, are additional points to confirm its identity. The female is similar, but her crest and pectoral plumes are less developed. The heron is normally seen as a solitary bird standing motionless in knee-deep water, head sunk between the shoulders and apparently fast asleep. All the while, however, it is fully alert and peering intently into the shallows for movement of any fish or frog that may blunder within striking range of its bill. On the quarry being sighted the bird cranes forward its long extensile neck with bill poised in readiness, and 'freezes'. Presently the rapier bill is thrust out with lightning speed to impale the victim or seize it in the mandibles. With a smart upward jerk it is manoeuvred into position and swallowed head foremost. In flight—attained by vigorous steady flapping of the wings—the neck is telescoped (as characteristic of the heron family) with the head drawn in between the shoulders; the long legs are tucked under the tail and trail behind. A deep harsh croak uttered on the wing from time to time is the only sound normally heard. The heron's nest is a twig platform with a central depression lined with grass etc. It is built in trees usually near water and often colonially in mixed heronries.

The eggs—3 to 6—are deep sea-green. The somewhat smaller **Purple Heron** (*A. purpurea*) of the same general appearance and habits, is also commonly met with in marshy habitats. It is bluish- or purplish grey above, with rufous head and neck; chestnut and black below.

Three species of white egrets—Large Egret, Median Egret, and Small Egret—are also commonly met with in marshy habitats similar to those which the heron frequents. The **Large Egret** (*Egretta alba*) is of about the size and build as the Purple Heron, pure snow white overall and usually solitary. The **Median** (*E. intermedia*) is slightly smaller, while the **Small Egret** (*E. garzetta*)—PLATE 6— Hindi: *Kǎrchia bǎgla* is about the size of a domestic hen, or of the Cattle Egret described further on. In the breeding season all the white egrets develop ornamental lacy plumes on their back which were in great demand for millinery purposes in Europe and America during the early years of the present century to pander to fashion in women's dress. The trade in feathers was so lucrative, and the birds were slaughtered for it in such vast numbers that egrets reached the point of extinction in many parts of the world. Only an international embargo on the traffic in wild birds' feathers, and bird protective legislation in the various affected countries, followed by a healthy change in women's fashions, has saved egrets from complete extinction. The **Cattle Egret** (*Bubulcus ibis*)—PLATE 7—Hindi: *Sūrhkia bǎgla* or *Gāi bǎgla* is a white bird very similar to the Little Egret but can always be distinguished from it in the non-breeding season by its stouter *yellow* (not black) bill. In its breeding plumage the orange-buff or golden head, neck, and back make its identity unmistakable. It is also less dependent than the Little Egret and other marsh-haunting relatives on the presence of water, and found most often singly or gregariously in attendance on grazing cattle. Its food consists largely of terrestrial insects. The birds stalk jauntily among the animals, running in and out between their legs—springing up to snatch the quarry as they scurry alongside—or riding on their backs for a better survey of the surroundings. They keep a vigilant lookout for the grasshoppers and other insects disturbed in the animal's progress through the grass, darting out their long projectile necks and pointed bills to snap them up as they flee. They also pick off blood-sucking flies and other parasitic insects from the backs, bellies and ears of the cattle, working complacently along the animal's back to reach the less accessible parts. Cattle egrets have communal roosts in favourite trees, shared with crows, pond herons and other birds, to which they repair every evening at sunset flying in diagonal lines or disorderly rabbles with the neck folded back, head hunched between the shoulders, and legs tucked under the tail and projecting behind. They breed in colonies by themselves or more usually in the company of pond herons; sometimes in mixed heronries with darters, cormorants, and white egrets. The nest is an untidy flimsy structure of twigs, of the usual crow pattern. It is built in leafy trees not necessarily in the neighbourhood of water and often in the midst of a noisy town or village bazar. The normal clutch is of 3 to 5 eggs of a pale skim-milk blue colour.

Another familiar member of the heron family is the **Pond Heron** or **Paddy Bird** (*Ardeola grayii*)—PLATE 8—known in Hindi in certain parts as *Āndhā bāglā*. It is about the size of a village hen, buff-streaked earthy brown when at rest but with concealed glistening white wings and tail which flash into prominence the moment the bird flies. In the breeding season the back is covered with dainty maroon hair-like plumes, and a long white occipital crest is acquired, transforming the drab-looking bird into a strikingly handsome creature. The Pond Heron may be seen singly or in twos and threes at muddy ponds and puddles and wherever conditions are favourable for harbouring frogs, mudfish and crabs which principally constitute its diet. Kutcha wells and temple ponds often in the heart of populous cities also attract it, and numbers collect at drying-up monsoon puddles to feast on the concentrating population of refugee frogs. The bird stands hunched up and inert on the squelchy mud or in shallow water at the edge, head drawn in between the shoulders. Actually it is wide awake and watching intently for some unsuspecting frog or fish to blunder within range of the long projectile neck and spear-pointed bill. Sometimes it will wade in stealthily, lifting each foot clear of the water and bringing it down with studied circumspection, neck craned forward and bill poised in readiness to jab at the quarry. Where unmolested pond herons become very tame and confiding, standing by the water's edge or stalking unconcernedly within a few feet of the village dhobi bashing his clothes, and of chattering house-wives filling their domestic pots. When alarmed it rises with a harsh croak and a sudden flash of its snow white wings and flies off with steady strokes in the typical heron style. Large congregations collect to roost in favourite trees at dusk. They build the usual crow type of twig nest in large trees often standing in the midst of towns and villages, and not necessarily close to water. They are frequently placed in mixed colonies of white egrets, night herons, etc., and the same trees are resorted to year after year. The eggs—3 to 5— are pale greenish blue.

Storks (family CICONIIDAE) are superficially similar to the larger herons. They have long legs with partially bare tibia, longish necks, and heavy, pointed tapering bills. In flight they can be readily told from herons by their outstretched necks *contra* herons which carry their necks telescoped in a flat S. Storks lack voice muscles and are therefore silent except for occasional low throaty grunts and a loud clattering together of the mandibles in which both sexes freely indulge during the breeding season. One of the more striking and common members of the family in India is the **Painted Stork** (*Ibis leucoce-phalus*)—PLATE 9—Hindi: *Jănghil, Dōkh, Kănkāri*. It is about the size of a vulture and stands some 3½ feet to the top of its head. Its white plumage is closely marked and barred above with glistening greenish black, and it has a black band across the breast. The striking delicate rose-pink feathers near the tail (secondaries) are what give it its name. The face is unfeathered waxy yellow and the heavy yellow bill slightly decurved at the tip. The birds are found in small parties or large gatherings at jheels and marshes. In common with other storks they spend the day standing hunched up and motionless or sauntering about sedately on marshland or in shallow water in search of fish and frogs which predominate on their menu; this also includes aquatic insects, crabs, and snails. The method of feeding in shallow water is to wade in and walk slowly with neck craned down, bill open and partly immersed. It is held thus, 'frozen' expectantly or swivelled from side to side while one foot is raised and waggled back

and forth to agitate the water and drive the quarry towards the open
mandibles. The foot-waggling is often accompanied by a sudden
flicking open of the wing on the same side, flashing its shadow on the
water and thus apparently speeding the movement of the prey. The
birds perch freely and roost in trees standing in or near water. Their
flight consists of a series of powerful wing strokes followed by a short
glide, and they have the usual stork habit of soaring and sailing in
circles high up in the air for long periods during the heat of the
day. The nest is a large stick platform with a shallow central
depression lined with stems and leaves of water weeds. It is built in
trees standing in or near water—often 10 to 20 nests in a single
tree—and in mixed heronries of cormorants, egrets, etc. The
eggs—3 to 5—are dull sullied white, occasionally with sparse spots
and streaks.

Perhaps the commonest and most widely distributed of our storks is
the much smaller **Openbilled Stork** (*Anastomus oscitans*)— PLATE 10—
Hindi: *Gūngla* or *Ghūngil*, which stands about 2½ feet to the crown. It
is white or greyish white in colour with black in the wings, sometimes
looking confusingly like the migratory White Stork in the distance.
The peculiar reddish black bill with arching mandibles leaving a
narrow open gap in between, is an unfailing diagnostic feature. The
bird is usually seen at jheels and marshes in twos and threes or flocks.
Its general habits and behaviour are typical of the stork family, but
the precise significance and function of the curiously shaped bill is
not properly understood. Essentially it is an adaptation for dealing
with the large snails which form its specialized diet. The gap in the
bill apparently helps the bird to crack the rim of the mouth of the
shell for prising open the 'lid' or operculum. The soft body of the
animal is neatly extracted from within and swallowed. Frogs, fish,
crabs, large insects and other small living things are also eaten.
Openbills breed in colonies, often very large ones, in association with
cormorants, herons, ibises, and other marsh birds. The nests are
rough circular platforms of twigs with the central depression lined
with leaves and stems of water weeds. They are placed—often many
together on a single tree—on trees standing within or on the edge of

a jheel, sometimes close to a village. The eggs—3 or 4—are sullied white without any markings.

The largest of our storks is the **Adjutant Stork** (*Leptoptilos dubius*)— PLATE 11—known in Hindi as *Hărgila, Gărūr*, or *Dhēnk*. It stands about 4 feet tall. The Adjutant is a huge sad-coloured black, grey, and dirty white stork with a ponderous yellow, four-sided, wedge-shaped bill. The long, naked, ruddy pouch about 12 inches long which hangs from its chest confirms its identity. It is usually seen singly or in small numbers on drying-up marshes and about municipal refuse dumps in some localities. The bird gets its appropriate English name from the deliberate high-stepping military gait with which it paces up and down in search of food. The true significance of the pendent pouch is not understood, but it is apparently in the nature of an air sac connected with the nasal cavity and not with the gullet. Therefore it cannot receive and store food as is popularly supposed. In addition to offal and garbage, the adjutant stork frequently joins vultures to feast on carrion. It also eats dead or stranded fish, frogs, reptiles and small animals, as well as locusts and other large insects. Its flight is heavy and noisy and the bird is obliged to take a short run with a vigorous flapping of the wings before getting air-borne. Like its other relations it is fond of soaring aloft on thermals and circling in the heavens on a sunny day. A very characteristic pose of the bird at rest is shown in the background of the plate—squatting with the shanks extended in front, head drawn in between the shoulders, presenting a ludicrously pathetic figure! The nest is an enormous structure of sticks built on pinnacles of rock or in lofty forest trees, sometimes in scattered colonies. The eggs—3 or 4—are white, usually much sullied.

A smaller cousin, the **Lesser Adjutant** (*L. javanicus*) occurs sparingly over a wide area including Kerala and Ceylon. It is chiefly glossy metallic black above, white below, and lacks the hanging pouch.

The family THRESKIORNITHIDAE is represented by the ibises and the spoonbill. The **White Ibis** (*Threskiornis melanocephala*)—

Hindi : *Mūnda, Mūndūkh,* or *Sāfēd Bāza* is a large white marsh bird of about the size of a large domestic hen, with naked black head and neck, and long, stout, black downcurved bill. In the breeding season some slaty grey appears on the scapulars and wings (secondaries), and long ornamental plumes at the base of the neck. It keeps in parties, sometimes large flocks, on marshland and the edges of jheels. It consorts with spoonbills, storks and similar birds, walking about actively on marshy grassland and squelchy paddy stubbles probing with the forceps-like half open mandibles into the soft mud for food. When feeding thus in shallow water the head is often completely immersed. Its food consists mainly of molluscs, crustaceans, worms, insects, frogs, and occasionally fish. When disturbed, and for roosting, the birds perch freely on trees. The flight is strong and direct with the long bill and neck extended in front and the legs trailing under the tail. It is attained by a series of steady rapid strokes punctuated by short glides. The birds usually fly to and from their feeding grounds in V-formation like ducks, or in wavy diagonal ribbons. Like storks and spoonbills they lack true voice organs, but breeding birds emit peculiar ventriloquistic grunts, not loud but vibrant. When heard from a distant colony they have been likened to the mumble of people talking together.

The nest is a flat platform of sticks, usually unlined, built in trees standing in or near water, sometimes on the outskirts of a village and often in mixed colonies with its usual feeding associates and with cormorants and darters. The eggs—2 to 4—are bluish or greenish white, either immaculate or marked with delicate spots of yellowish brown.

The **Black Ibis** (*Pseudibis papillosa*)—PLATE 12—Hindi: *Kālā bāzā* or *Kărānkūl,* is a largish black bird of about the same size and general aspect as the White Ibis. It has a conspicuous white patch near the shoulder, and brick-red legs. The naked black head with a triangular patch of crimson warts on the crown is another good distinguishing mark. The birds are found in open plains country on the outskirts of cultivation where they keep in small parties of 3 or 4 and scattered flocks of up to 8 or 10 individuals. Unlike the White Ibis it is less dependent on the neighbourhood of jheels and rivers and is frequently found well away from water. Its food consists principally of insects and grain, but lizards, small snakes and centipedes are also relished. The birds keep to favoured localities and have accustomed roosts in trees to which they resort nightly, flying in V-formation by a series of steady wing strokes alternated with short glides. They are silent birds on the whole, only occasionally uttering a loud nasal screaming cry of 2 or 3 notes, chiefly on the wing. These cries are rather reminiscent of those of the Brahminy Duck. Black Ibises normally do not breed in mixed colonies, but two or three nests of its own species may sometimes be found in the same tree. The nest is a large cup-shaped structure of twigs lined with straw and feathers. It is placed high up in a large tree or in the head of a palmyra palm generally away from water. Occasionally old nests of eagles or vultures are utilized. The eggs—2 to 4—are bright pale green in colour, either unmarked or with spots and streaks of brown.

Though a close relation of the ibises, the **Spoonbill** (*Platalea leucorodia*)—PLATE 13—Hindi : *Chămchā bāzā* or *Dābil*, has an entirely different shaped and very distinctive bill; it is black-and-yelow, broad and flat, and ends in a widened spatula. The bird itself—larger than a domestic duck and standing about 18 inches tall—is long-legged, long-necked and snow white. A long and full pale yellow nuchal crest, and a yellow patch on the lower foreneck, are acquired in the breeding season. The birds are usually met with singly or in flocks of 10 to 20 or more by themselves or in association with storks and other marsh birds. Although the species is resident in India, its numbers are greatly augmented in winter by immigrants from beyond our limits. The Spoonbill affects marshes and jheels, mudbanks in rivers, and estuarine mudflats. The birds feed in shallow water at the edge, and are most active in the mornings and evenings, resting on some sandbank during the middle of the day. They fly to and from their feeding grounds in diagonal single file or in orderly V-formation with rather slow but steady wing beats—neck and legs extended—and often at a considerable height. Their food consists of tadpoles, frogs, molluscs and water insects, but a quantity of vegetable matter is also taken. The flock wades into shallow water at the edge of a jheel,

M

0   10 CM

PLATE 1
LITTLE GREBE or DABCHICK
(*Podiceps ruficollis*)
(*see* page 21)

PLATE 2

SPOTTEDBILLED or GREY PELICAN
(*Pelecanus philippensis*)
(*see* page 22)

PLATE 3
DARTER
(*Anhinga rufa*)
(*see* page 23)

PLATE 4
LITTLE CORMORANT
(*Phalacrocorax niger*)
(*see* page 24)

PLATE 5
GREY HERON
(*Ardea cinerea*)
(*see* page 25)

PLATE 6
SMALL EGRET
(Egretta garzetta)
(see page 26)

PLATE 7

CATTLE EGRET
(Bubulcus ibis)
(see page 26)

PLATE 8
POND HERON or PADDY BIRD
(*Ardeola grayii*)
(*see* page 27)

PLATE 9

PAINTED STORK

(Ibis leucocephalus)

(see page 28)

PLATE 10
OPENBILLED STORK
(*Anastomus oscitans*)
(*see* page 29)

PLATE 11
ADJUTANT STORK
(*Leptoptilos dubius*)
(*see* page 30)

PLATE 12
BLACK IBIS
(*Pseudibis papillosa*)
(*see* page 31)

PLATE 13
SPOONBILL
(*Platalea leucorodia*)
(*see* page 32)

PLATE 14
FLAMINGO
(*Phoenicopterus roseus*)
(*see* page 33)

PLATE 15

BARHEADED GOOSE

(Anser indicus)
(see page 34)

PLATE 16

SPOTBILL or GREY DUCK

(*Anas poecilorhyncha*)

(*see* page 35)

and with outstretched neck and obliquely poised partly open bill
the birds sweep from side to side with a scything action raking
the muddy bottom with the tip of the lower mandible. The compact
eager jostling herd moves forward thus, almost at a run, working
methodically up and down the more rewarding patches. The only
sound the bird occasionally emits is a low grunt. Spoonbills nest in
colonies either by themselves or in association with herons, ibises,
cormorants, egrets and storks. The nest is a rather massive stick
platform built in a tree standing in or on the edge of a jheel—
frequently on the outskirts of a village. The normal clutch is of
4 eggs, sullied white in colour, sparingly spotted and blotched with
deep reddish brown.

The only representative of the family PHOENICOPTERIDAE in India
is the **Flamingo** (*Phoenicopterus roseus*)— PLATE 14—Hindi: *Bōg hăns,
Chărăj băggo*. It is a pale rosy-white bird with the body as large as a
domestic goose, long bare pink legs and long sinuous neck so that the
bird stands about 4 feet high. The peculiar heavy pink bill turned
down at an angle ('broken') from about half its length is unique,
and the toes are webbed like a duck's. A flock in the air with the
brilliant scarlet wing-coverts set off by the black wing border presents
a spectacle of unforgettable charm. Flamingos live in flocks at jheels,
brackish lagoons, and on tidal mudflats. They are resident more or
less throughout the Indian Union, both Pakistans and Ceylon but
sporadic, and also locally migratory. The birds keep in small parties
or flocks, some of very large size and containing many thousand
individuals. Their method of procuring their food is to wade into
shallow water and feed with their long necks bent down and heads
completely immersed. The peculiar bill is inverted so that the top
part of the culmen almost scrapes the ground agitating the bottom
mud. In this position the upper mandible forms a hollow scoop in
which the ooze is collected. The fleshy tongue works like a plunger,
sieving out the water through the comb-like fringes or lamellae along
the edge of the mandibles leaving the minute food particles behind.
The birds can swim with ease when occasion demands, and when
feeding in deeper water they often 'up-end' like ducks with only the

tail sticking above the surface, in order to reach the bottom mud. The food consists of tiny crustaceans, insect larvae, worms, seeds of marsh plants, and organic ooze. Flamingos fly with fairly rapid wing beats in V-formation, like geese, or in long wavy diagonal ribbons. The slender neck is stretched in front while the long red legs trail behind. The birds are on the whole very silent. They sometimes utter a goose-like *honk*, and a flock keeps up a constant babble while feeding. The only known breeding place of the Flamingo within our limits is the Great Rann of Kutch where vast concentrations collect between October and March when the water conditions are favourable. Their numbers here have been estimated at between half and one million strong, thus making the Kutch breeding colony, or 'Flamingo City', perhaps the largest in the world. The nest is a cone-shaped mound of scraped-up and plastered semi-liquid mud which becomes hard and sun-baked and has an average height of about a foot. A flat pan-cake like depression is tamped on the top in which the eggs—2, or only 1—are laid. The incubating Flamingo sits on this with its legs folded under, and not standing astride the mound as was fancifully described in old books.

The Order ANSERIFORMES comprises a very popular group of birds from the sporting and food resource point of view. It includes swans, geese, and ducks. Teals are merely small ducks just as doves are small pigeons, and differ from ducks only in name.

Swans are erratic vagrants from arctic Europe and Asia in years of extreme winters and need not be considered here. Among the few species of geese that visit our area in winter one of the commonest and most regular is the **Barheaded Goose** (*Anser indicus*)—PLATE 15— Hindi : *Hăns, Săwăn, Bīrwă*. Its size is about that of a small domestic goose, and its coloration chiefly grey, brownish, and white. The white head and sides of neck, yellow bill, and two distinctive broad black bars across the nape are the points by which it can be identi-fied. It is found in flocks or gaggles on rivers and jheels and in the neighbourhood of young wheat and gram fields. It keeps in small parties and skeins of 15 to 20 individuals, sometimes congregating in vast gaggles to feed in young gram and wheat fields or rest in the mid-day heat on a sandbank in a river. On account of constant harrass-ment from hunters the bird is largely crepuscular or nocturnal in its feeding habits. It becomes active towards sunset when flock after flock may be seen winging its way steadily in orderly V-formation or diagonal ribbons high up in the air in the direction of the accustomed feeding grounds. Like all geese, the birds feed by grazing as they walk about in the fields or by 'up-ending' in shallow water. Their food consists largely of green shoots of winter crops, grain, corns of marsh plants, etc.

The call is a musical *aang*, *aang* produced in varying keys which is one of the most exhilarating and nerve-tingling sounds to the wildfowler as the birds pass over his ambush. The Barhead is at all times an exceedingly wary species and calls for much skill and hard work in circumventing and bringing to bag. Curiously enough, where the same birds have learnt they will not be molested, as in Buddhist Tibet, they become astonishingly tame and confiding and will stroll about unconcernedly in the proximity of yakmen's encamp-ments.

The nearest breeding grounds of the Barheaded Goose are in Ladakh. The nest is a depression in the lush herbage bordering the high altitude lakes, thickly lined with down and feathers. The eggs—3 or 4—are ivory white.

Another common migrant goose is the **Greylag** (*Anser anser*)—Hindi : *Kāj*—believed to be the ancestor of practically all our domestic breeds. Its size and general effect are those of the normal brown phase of the domestic goose. It has a grey rump and a flesh-pink bill, and it keeps more to jheels than to rivers unlike the Barhead.

Only 5 or 6 of the 20 odd species of wild ducks commonly found in India in winter are resident and breed within the country; the rest are migrants chiefly from Siberia. One of the most widely distributed of the former is the **Spotbill** or **Grey Duck** (*Anas poecilorhyncha*)—PLATE 16—Hindi : *Gărmpāi, Gūgrāl, Lăddim*. In size it is as large as the domestic

duck and of a scaly-patterned light and dark brown plumage. The
tri-coloured white, black, and metallic green wing-bar or speculum
are leading pointers to its identity. This is confirmed by the bright
orange-red legs, and yellow-tipped dark bill with two orange-red
spots at its base, one on either side of the forehead. It is found in pairs
and small flocks on shallow reedy jheels, but is nowhere as abundant
as many of the migratory species that visit us in winter.   It belongs
to the tribe of surface-feeding or dabbling ducks and obtains
much of its food by walking about and grubbing on marshland
or in squelchy paddy fields, or by 'up-ending' in shallow water to
reach the bottom mud—tail sticking comically above the surface and
legs kicking to maintain the vertical stance. The Spotbill's food is
chiefly vegetarian—shoots of aquatic plants, seeds of sedges, and
paddy grain with the addition of molluscs, water insects, and worms.
It is a strong flier and prized by sportsmen as much for its sporting
qualities as for its excellence as a table bird. Normally the birds are
very silent. The call of the drake is a harsh wheezing; that of the duck
a loud quack, chiefly uttered on sudden alarm. Given favourable
water conditions the Spotbill breeds more or less throughout the year.
The nest is a pad of grass and weeds sometimes lined with feathers
and down, concealed under herbage on the edge of a tank or swamp.
The eggs—7 to 9 and up to 12—are greyish buff or greenish white,
without any markings.

The **Lesser Whistling Teal** (*Dendrocygna javanica*)—PLATE 17—
Hindi : *Silhi* or *Silkāhi*, is smaller than the Spotbill of a more or less
uniform chestnut colour and confusable with no other duck of the
same size. The shrill whistling notes uttered in the rail-like flight are
also distinctive. It is found in small flocks of 10 or 15 on all reed and
floating vegetation-covered tanks and jheels, and often also in swampy
paddy fields. It is partial to such as have trees growing around them,
on the branches of which it perches freely—a habit which gives it
its alternative name of Fulvous Tree Duck. The birds move about
a great deal locally under stress of drought conditions. The flight is
feeble and flapping, rather reminiscent of a jaçana's—and is accompanied by a constant shrill wheezy whistling *sea-sick*, *sea-sick* rather

similar to some notes of the Large Pied Wagtail. The birds walk well and are good divers. Their food consists of snails, worms, frogs, and fish, as well as green shoots and paddy grains. The nest of the Whistling Teal is either a pad of leaves, rushes, and grass placed on the ground among thorny scrub near the water's edge, or a twig structure in forking trunks or natural hollows in large trees, often well away from water. Old nests of kites and crows are sometimes utilized. The eggs—7 to 12, but usually about 10—are milk-white in colour when fresh, but become stained brownish during incubation.

The **Large Whistling Teal** (*D. bicolor*), also found sparingly as a resident in India, is distinguished from the Lesser by its somewhat larger size and by its upper tail-coverts being *whitish* instead of chestnut in colour.

The smallest of our resident wild ducks is the **Cotton Teal** (*Nettapus coromandelianus*)—PLATE 18—Hindi : *Girria, Gūrgūra, Sōnia*. It is the size of a small village hen with white predominating in its plumage. The drake is glossy blackish above, with white head, neck, and underparts. It has a narrow black collar, and a white wing-bar which is conspicuous in flight. The duck is paler brown and without the collar or wing-bar. In the non-breeding season the drake resembles her except for the white wing-bar which is retained. The Cotton Teal is not only the smallest but also the most widely distributed of our resident ducks, sharing this attribute with the Spotbill. It is usually met with in parties of 5 or 15 or so, but larger flocks of up to 50 or more are occasionally seen. It affects every type of stagnant water provided it is well covered with reeds and floating vegetation—be it village tank, roadside ditch, flooded borrow-pit or inundated paddy field. Where unmolested the birds become very tame and trusting, swimming and tipping for food on village ponds within a few feet of humans engaged in their daily avocations. Their food consists of shoots and grain together with insects, snails, etc. The birds are swift and agile on the wing, and can dive effectively to evade capture when moulting and flightless. A peculiar clucking, uttered in flight, is practically all the sound they produce. The nest of the Cotton Teal is some natural hollow in a tree-trunk standing in or near water, 6 to 30 feet above the surface. The eggs—6 to 12—are ivory white, unmarked. The downy hatchlings are not carried down by the parents as generally believed, but flutter to the ground or water by themselves.

The Order FALCONIFORMES or Birds of Prey is represented by the families ACCIPITRIDAE (hawks, eagles, vultures, and osprey) and the FALCONIDAE (falcons). No hard and fast limits can be fixed between the two. Both are characterized by a short and strongly hooked bill for tearing flesh, and powerful hooked claws. The former family contains broad and rounded-winged birds, the latter those with longer, narrow and pointed wings and more spindle-shaped bodies, streamlined for extreme speed in chasing prey. Some of these birds (*e.g.* kites and vultures) feed on offal and carrion while others like the shikra and sparrow-hawks chiefly hunt living prey by pouncing on it from an ambush, sometimes followed by a short swift chase. The falcons, on the other hand are essentially hunters which secure their quarry by swift pursuit and lightning aerial stoop from above. Accordingly hawks live chiefly in wooded country affording concealment while falcons are more at home in open unobstructed terrain.

As a group, hawks, eagles, and falcons have been unjustly maligned for alleged destruction of game birds and ground game. In official game schedules they are usually classed as vermin and afforded no legal protection. A careful study of their food and feeding habits, however, indicates that by preying predominantly on rats and mice, and other injurious pests, most species act as very important natural checks. On balance, therefore, the birds of prey are decidedly more beneficial than harmful, and deserving of strict statutory protection.

The **Pariah** and **Brahminy Kites**—PLATES 19 AND 20—are two familiar hawks that live in the neighbourhood of human habitations and here depend for their livelihood chiefly on the artificial conditions

created by man. The former is a large brown hawk easily distinguished from all other similar birds by its *forked* tail, a feature particularly noticeable in flight. Numbers are always present near
slaughter houses, fish and meat markets, municipal refuse dumps and
around docks and harbours for any titbits that can be picked up. The
ease and grace with which a kite will make its lightning swoop to
carry off a dead rat or bit of offal from a narrow congested city bazar,
turning and twisting to avoid the pedestrians and motor traffic on the
ground and the tangle of telephone wires overhead, is an object
lesson in aeronautics. The bird becomes a nuisance to poultry keepers
when it takes to chicken-lifting as it often does when it has its nest-
young to feed. Its shrill musical whistle *ewe-wir-wir-wir-wir* is familiar
to most town dwellers.

The **Brahminy Kite** (*Haliastur indus*), known in Hindi as *Brāhmăni
cheel, Dhōbia cheel*, or *Khemkărni*, is of the same size but distinctly more
handsome. It is bright rusty red above, with a white head and breast
down to the abdomen. Immature birds are chocolate brown and
resemble both the Pariah Kite and the young Scavenger Vulture.
It may be readily differentiated from them by its *rounded* instead of
forked or wedge-shaped tail respectively. The Brahminy keeps to the
neighbourhood of rivers and tanks inland, but is commonest on the
sea coast where it frequents fishing villages and harbours. During the
monsoon, when large tracts become waterlogged, it spreads further
afield and is then commonly seen around inundated paddy fields.
Its diet also consists of offal and garbage and it freely enters human
habitations to scavenge in company with Pariah Kites and crows.
But it prefers to scoop up its food from the surface of water rather
than land, and therefore sea ports and fishing docks are best suited
to its requirements. On the countryside it lives chiefly on lizards,
fish, frogs, land crabs, small snakes, as well as insects. Like the
Pariah Kite it is specially partial to winged termites which are
clumsily hawked in the air as they emerge from the rain-sodden
ground. Its call is a rather harsh wheezy squeal—rather like a
kite suffering from sore throat. Both these hawks build large stick
platform nests in trees, the Brahminy preferring those in the neigh-

bourhood of water. Their eggs are greyish or pinkish white speckled and spotted with reddish brown.

The **Shikra** (*Accipiter badius*)—PLATE 21—Hindi: *Shikra* is a smaller hawk, about the size of a pigeon, ashy blue-grey above, white below cross-barred with rusty brown and with broad blackish bands on the tail. The female is browner above and considerably larger than the male. Immature birds are brown-and-rufous above, broadly streaked below (not cross-barred) with brown. It is usually met with in pairs in wooded country and groves of trees in the neighbourhood of villages and cultivation. The food of the Shikra consists of locusts, lizards, frogs, rats, and the like. Its hunting tactics are mainly those of surprise. From its lookout perch in the concealment of some leafy tree, where it sits bolt upright, the bird pounces upon its victims before they become aware of danger, and bears them away in its talons to be plucked and torn to pieces before devouring. It also kills small birds like babblers, bush quails and doves, swooping on them from its ambush without warning and chasing them with speed and determination. The Shikra is an inveterate robber of domestic chickens, especially when it has its nest-young to feed, and often becomes a serious nuisance to poultry keepers. Many of its harsh challenging call notes are exactly like those of the Black Drongo but louder. During the breeding season pairs become very noisy, constantly uttering a sharp double note *ti-tui* as the birds go through a curious aerobatic display, mutually chasing and diving at each other. The Shikra builds a crow-like nest of twigs in the top of a leafy tree preferably standing in a grove near a village. Its eggs—3 or 4—are pale bluish white, sometimes faintly spotted and speckled with grey.

The commonest vulture over the country as a whole is the **White-backed** or **Bengal Vulture** (*Gyps bengalensis*)—PLATE 22—Hindi: *Gidh*, a heavy dirty blackish brown rather repulsive-looking creature, with scrawny naked head and neck. When at rest and while banking in the air the white back is conspicuous and diagnostic. In overhead flight a broad whitish band stretching across the underside

of the wings, broken in the middle by the dark body, helps identification. Immature birds are brown without the white back and
can be easily confused with another common species, the **Longbilled
Vulture** (*G. indicus*). Strangely enough neither of these vultures
is found in Ceylon. The Whitebacked Vulture is found everywhere
in peninsular India regardless of the nature of the country, but it
avoids humid evergreen forest. It quarters the heavens sailing
majestically for hours on end on outspread motionless wings, scanning
the countryside for food. As scavengers, vultures are of the greatest
usefulness to man. Their eyesight is remarkably keen, and sense
of smell poor or non-existent. The incredibly short time in which a
rabble will collect at an animal carcase from out of an almost empty
sky is a thing of wonder, and the speed and thoroughness with
which such a gathering will dispose of a bullock or other large
animal is equally astonishing. The gruesome obsequies at a carcase
are attended by incessant jostling and bickering among the feasters
and much raucous screeching and hissing as one bird tries to oust
another from a vantage point, or as two birds ludicrously prance
around with outspread wings tugging and pulling at a gobbet of
flesh from either end. This vulture nests in large trees standing
near a village or along the sides of roads, building enormous platforms of leafy sticks and twigs. A single egg is laid, white in coloration, sometimes speckled and spotted with reddish brown.

A smaller vulture, common in the drier portions of the Peninsula,
is the **White** or **Scavenger Vulture** also known as **Pharaoh's
Chicken** (*Neophron percnopterus*) and in Hindi as *Sāfēd gidh* or *Gōbăr
gidh*—PLATE 23. It is a dirty white kite-like bird with black wing
quills and naked sickly yellow head and bill. Immature birds are
brown but may be distinguished from the kite in flight by the
wedge-shaped, not forked tail. They are usually seen in twos and threes
in open country about human habitations—whether town, settled
village or nomadic encampment—soaring gracefully high up in
the heavens or scouting for food lower down. On the ground it
stalks about in the quest with a ludicrous high-stepping waddling
gait. It is a useful scavenger and does valuable service in cleaning up

the precincts of villages where for lack of proper sanitation the
entire populace is obliged to troop out with their domestic *lotas*
and squat behind bushes at no great distance from their hovels.
For besides offal and refuse of every description, human excrement
figures largely on this vulture's delectable menu. This, incidentally,
is the species that has brought fame to the Hindu temple at Thiru-
kalikundram near Madras where a legendary immortal pair comes
at a regular hour every day (from Banaras as the credulous believe)
to be fed by the priests. The nest is a filthy mass of twigs lined with
rags, scraps of mammal skin, hair and miscellaneous rubbish. It is
placed on a ledge outside a ruined building, or a rock cliff; sometimes in a forking tree-stem. The eggs, normally two, are in-
congruously handsome—white to pale brick-red, blotched with
reddish brown or blackish.

A good example of the pointed-winged hawks is the **Shaheen
Falcon** (*Falco peregrinator*)—PLATE 24—Hindi: *Shaheen* a powerful,
compact, broad-shouldered bird about the size of a Jungle Crow.
Adults are slaty black above with a black head and prominent
cheek-stripes; pinky white or rusty red below. Some examples are
barred with black from the abdomen down. The female is similar
but larger. The Shaheen is found singly or in pairs in hilly country
with precipices and crags whence it keeps a lookout for prey and
launches its foraging sorties. It is the local representative of the
Peregrine Falcon or *Bhyri* which is a winter visitor to our area from
northern lands. Its prey consists chiefly of pigeons, parakeets and
similar sized birds. The flight of the Shaheen is extremely swift—
a few rapid beats of the pointed wings followed by a glide at
tremendous speed. Its victims are struck in mid-air and borne away
in the talons to a favourite cliff where they are plucked of their
feathers and dismembered before being swallowed. During the
breeding season pairs engage in a great deal of spectacular aerial
interplay, the birds darting and stooping at each other at breath-
taking speed around the nesting cliff, often executing perfect looping-the-loop turns. They nest on inaccessible crags laying 3 or 4
pale brick-red eggs, blotched and speckled with reddish brown.

The same nest sites are used year after year for long periods, and if undisturbed become traditional.

The **Redheaded Merlin** (*Falco chicquera*) or *Tūrūmti*—PLATE 25— is an elegant little pointed-winged falcon, bluish grey above, white below, closely cross-barred with blackish on the underparts. The conspicuous chestnut head and nape, with a vertical chestnut 'moustachial' streak below and in front of each eye, are good identification marks. In flight the narrow white border to the tail with a broad black band above it are other points to look for. The birds are usually found in pairs in open country near cultivation, commonly seen perched on a mound or some other eminence, or flying at great speed at hedge-top height in search of small birds, rats, mice, lizards and large insects which comprise their prey. It sometimes catches bats as they emerge from their daytime retreat at dusk, stooping at them with incredible speed. Male and female often hunt in concert, one bird driving and rounding off the quarry while the other chases and strikes it down, the two then share the spoils. The larger female (*tūrūmti*) is sometimes trained to hunt such birds as rollers, hoopoes, mynas and partridges. When in pursuit, the flight is very swift and arrow-like, attained by rapid and sustained wing-beats as in the Sparrow-Hawk. Its cry is a high-pitched squeal. During the breeding season these little falcons become exceedingly bold and truculent, attacking and beating off large birds like crows and kites who have blundered into the vicinity of the nest tree. The nest is a twig platform up in the leafy canopy of a tree standing in open country. The eggs —3 or 4— are pale reddish white, thickly speckled with reddish brown.

The Order GALLIFORMES is represented in our area chiefly by the family PHASIANIDAE or the so-called 'Game Birds' which includes pheasants, junglefowl, partridges and quails. They are predominantly granivorous birds with strong moderate sized bills, rounded wings, sturdy short to moderately long legs (armed with spurs in the males of many species), and stout blunt claws for scratching the ground for food.

The **Black Partridge** (*Francolinus francolinus*)—PLATE 26—Hindi: *Kālā teetăr*, is about the same size as the better known Grey Partridge. It is a plump, stub-tailed game bird chiefly jet black, spotted and barred with white and fulvous. The glistening white cheek-patches and chestnut collar of the cock are diagnostic. The hen is considerably paler, mottled and speckled black and white, with a chestnut patch on the nape. This handsome partridge is found singly or in pairs in well-watered scrub-, tamarisk-, and tall grass jungle and river-ain tracts in northern India and Assam. Sugarcane fields, standing millet crops, and tea gardens are some of its other favourite haunts. The birds enter the crops to feed in the early mornings and evenings when they may also be seen pecking around the edges of the fields. While sauntering about, the stub tail is often carried partially cocked, as in a moorhen, a peculiarity not normally seen in the Grey Partridge. They are exceedingly swift runners and will usually trust to their legs for escape unless driven by beaters or suddenly come upon. The flight, usually of not more than a couple of hundred metres at a stretch, is strong and direct with rapid whirring wing beats, and seldom above 10 to 15 feet from the ground. The food consists of grain, grass- and weed seeds and tender shoots, but white ants and other insects are also relished. The call of the cock is a cheerful, ringing, high pitched *chik . . . cheek-cheek-keraykek*, a curious mixture of the harsh and the musical, and possesses a peculiar ventriloquistic quality. It has been rendered as *Sūbhān-tēri-qūdrăt*, *Lăsăn-piāz-ădrăk* and other variants according to the hearer's mood and fancy of the moment! The nest of the Black Partridge is a shallow grass-lined depression in the ground at the root of a grass clump, in tamarisk scrub or grassland. The eggs—6 to 8—vary in colour from pale olive-brown to almost chocolate brown.

The **Grey Partridge** (*Francolinus pondicerianus*)—PLATE 27—Hindi: *Teetăr* or *Sāfēd teetăr*, is about as large as a half-grown village hen of the same plump and stub-tailed appearance as the Black Partridge. It is greyish brown overall with fine wavy black-and-buff vermiculations, and some chestnut in the tail. The throat is rufous and encircled by a broken black line. The cock differs from the hen in being more robust, with a pointed spur on each leg. The Grey Partridge is a bird of dry open grass-and-thorn scrub country and commonly found in the neighbourhood of villages and cultivation. Its exhilarating ringing calls are amongst the most familiar bird sounds on the countryside. Except when paired off for breeding, the birds go about in coveys of 4 to 6, running about with a jaunty upright carriage and scratching the ground and cattle dung for food. This consists of seeds, berries and insects—white ants and maggots from human and animal excreta being favourite items. On alarm the covey scuttles away, running speedily from bush to bush, finally taking surreptitious refuge within the thickets in ones and twos. They are loth to fly unless pressed when they flush with a loud whirr of wings and scatter in different directions, running on immediately upon realighting a hundred metres or so further. They roost at night up in thorn trees. The call of the cock is a ringing, defiant, high-pitched *kăteetăr, kăteetăr*, etc. or *păteela, păteela, păteela* quickly repeated and rising in scale and intensity. Young birds can be readily tamed, and follow their master about like a dog, calling at his behest and coming long distances when summoned. The males are prized for fighting purposes. In some parts of the country partridge-fighting is a popular village sport on high days and holidays, and large wagers are won and lost on the mains. Champion birds command big prices. The nest of the Grey Partridge is a simple grass-lined scrape in the ground under shelter of a thorn bush in grass- or fallow land. The eggs—4 to 8—are brownish cream in colour, without any markings.

The **Blackbreasted** or **Rain Quail** (*Coturnix coromandelica*)—PLATE 28—Hindi: *Chănăk, Chină bătēr*, is about half the size of the Grey Partridge and a miniature of it in profile. Its plumage is buffy brown with pale streaks and irregular blackish blotches on the upper parts. The upper breast, and often the centre of the abdomen, is black in the cock. The hen lacks the black breast and the black-and-white markings on the throat.

The somewhat larger **Common** or **Grey Quail** (*C. coturnix*) is chiefly an abundant winter visitor from northern lands. In this species the cock has a black anchor mark on his throat and no black on the breast or belly. The hen is very like that of the Rain Quail only larger. In the hand she can be differentiated by the presence of buff and brown bars on the outer webs of the primaries. Both species have similar habits. Quails are ground-living birds which spend most of their time under cover in grassland or young crops. They are good runners and reluctant to fly unless pressed. When flushed they rise with a characteristic low whirr of the wings accompanied by a soft whistling note, and fly only a hundred metres or so, low over the grass-tops or standing crops before tumbling into cover again. The flight is swift and direct, attained by rapid 'vibrating' wing strokes. Their diet consists almost entirely of grain and grass- and weed seeds, supplemented by termites and other soft insects. The call of the Rain Quail is a musical double whistle *which-which ...which-which*, etc. constantly repeated in the breeding season chiefly in the mornings and evenings and intermittently all through the day in cloudy weather, and at night. It is quite distinct from the call of the Grey Quail which is a loud whistling note followed rapidly by two short ones, described as 'a liquid *wet-me-lips*.' The nests of both species are grass-lined scrapes, usually well concealed among grass or standing crops. The eggs—6 to 8—are pale creamy buff blotched with varying shades of brown and differ only in size.

The **Jungle Bush Quail** (*Perdicula asiatica*)—PLATE 29 —Hindi: *Lowwā*, is of the same size and general effect as the quails. The cock is fulvous-brown above, streaked and mottled with black and buff; white below, closely barred with black. The hen has the underparts pale pinkish rufous. Both sexes have a prominent buff and chestnut superciliary stripe running back from the forehead and down the sides of the neck; also a bright chestnut throat patch. A confusingly similar species, the **Rock Bush Quail** (*P. argoondah*) is often found side by side with it. In this the cock has the throat-patch dull brick-red instead of chestnut, and the hen lacks the throat-patch altogether. The Jungle Bush Quail is found in fairly open deciduous forest and dry grass-and-scrub jungle. It lives in coveys of 5 to 20 individuals which, when roosting at night or if disturbed during daytime, bunch together under a bush or in thin grass cover, all the birds facing outward. They suddenly rise together or 'explode' with a distracting whirr of wings when almost trodden on and disperse in all directions, dropping into cover again after a short flight. The covey soon reunites by means of soft whistling contact calls, *whi-whi-whi* etc. uttered by the members. The birds troop down to drink at water holes in single file in the mornings and evenings using the same little paths day after day. Their food consists mainly of grain, grass- and weed seeds, and shoots, together with termites and other insects. In the breeding season males become pugnacious and issue harsh grating challenges to rivals. The nest is a grass-lined scrape at the base of a grass-tussock in scrub jungle. The eggs—4 to 8—are creamy white without markings, and entirely different from those of the Rain Quail.

The **Grey Junglefowl** (*Gallus sonneratii*)—PLATE 30—Hindi: *Jāngli mūrghi* is, sex for sex, about the same size as the village *mūrghi*. The general effect of the cock is streaked grey with a metallic black sickle-shaped tail. The hen is brown above, largely white below with scale-like black markings. It is found singly or in pairs or small parties in broken foothills country with bamboo jungle, and is partial to the thick tangles of lantana and secondary scrub that spring up on the sites of old forest clearings, and to neglected or abandoned plantations. It is chiefly restricted to the western side of the Peninsula. Large numbers collect to feed in areas where bamboo or *karvi* thickets are in seed. Junglefowl, both this and the red species, are shy and timid birds. They emerge into the open to scratch the ground for food in the mornings and evenings, seldom straying far from cover and scuttling headlong into it on the least suspicion with outstretched neck and drooping tail. Their food consists of grain, shoots and berries such as lantana and ber (*Zizyphus*). Windfallen fruit, such as figs of the banyan and gulair (*Ficus* spp.) are highly relished, while insects, grubs and maggots are also eaten. The crow of the Grey Junglecock is well rendered as *kūck-kăyā-kăyā-kūk*. It ends with a low *kyukun-kyukun* repeated slowly and softly and audible only at short range. It is given from a mound, fallen tree-trunk, or some other eminence and is usually preceded by a loud clapping of the wings against the sides. The crowing is answered in turn by other cocks within hearing distance all round.

It is not quite certain whether junglecocks are monogamous or maintain a harem as some other game birds do. The nest is a shallow scrape in dense undergrowth, lined with dry leaves. The normal clutch consists of 4 to 7 eggs, pale to warm buff in colour, very like those of the country hen.

The **Red Junglefowl** (*G. gallus*)—the ancestor of all our domestic breeds—is found chiefly in the Himalayan terai and foothills extending south, almost coincidentally with the sāl tree (*Shorea robusta*) to eastern Madhya Pradesh. Both cock and hen look very like the Bantam breed of domestic poultry, and the cock's crow is also very similar.

The most familiar and spectacular member of the pheasant family in peninsular India is of course the **Common Peafowl** (*Pavo cristatus*)—PLATE 31—Hindi: *Mōr* or *Mǎyūr*, which has recently been 'elected' our National Bird.

It is sufficiently well known not to need describing, but what is not so generally realized is that the gorgeous ocellated, or 'eyed', train of the cock is actually not his tail but abnormally lengthened upper tail-coverts. The hen is crested like the cock but lacks the train and is a sober mottled brown with some metallic green on the lower neck. Peafowl are usually met with in parties or 'droves' of mixed sexes, chiefly in deciduous plains and foothills forest. At some seasons the cocks and hens tend to segregate. The birds emerge into forest clearings and fields to feed in the mornings and evenings. Those who only know peafowl in their semi-domesticated state in areas where they are protected by religious sentiment, as in Gujarat and Rajasthan, can have no idea of their uncanny wariness and cunning in the wild where subjected to hunting or normal natural predation. The birds are possessed of phenomenally keen eyesight and hearing and are almost impossible to take unawares, usually

PLATE 17
LESSER WHISTLING TEAL
(Dendrocygna javanica)
(*see* page 36)

PLATE 18
COTTON TEAL
(*Nettapus coromandelianus*)
(*see* page 37)

PARIAH KITE
(Milvus migrans)
(*see* page 38)

PLATE 20
BRAHMINY KITE
(*Haliastur indus*)
(*see* page 39)

PLATE 21
SHIKRA
(*Accipiter badius*)
(*see* page 40)

PLATE 22
WHITEBACKED or BENGAL VULTURE
(*Gyps bengalensis*)
(*see* page 40)

PLATE 23
WHITE or SCAVENGER VULTURE
(*Neophron percnopterus*)
(*see* page 41)

PLATE 24
SHAHEEN FALCON
(*Falco peregrinator*)
(*see* page 42)

PLATE 25
REDHEADED MERLIN
(*Falco chicquera*)
(*see* page 43)

PLATE 26
BLACK PARTRIDGE
(*Francolinus francolinus*)
(*see* page 44)

PLATE 27
GREY PARTRIDGE
(*Francolinus pondicerianus*)
(*see* page 44)

PLATE 28
BLACKBREASTED or RAIN QUAIL
(*Coturnix coromandelica*)
(*see* page 45)

PLATE 29
JUNGLE BUSH QUAIL
(*Perdicula asiatica*)
(*see* page 46)

PLATE 30
GREY JUNGLEFOWL
(*Gallus sonneratii*)
(*see* page 47)

PLATE 31
COMMON PEAFOWL
(*Pavo cristatus*)
(*see* page 48)

PLATE 32
SARAS CRANE
(*Grus antigone*)
(*see* page 49)

slinking away through the undergrowth for escape on the slightest suspicion. But when suddenly come upon or driven out of cover they rise with noisy laborious flapping often rocketing almost vertically and in spite of the cumbrous 'tail' develop considerable speed when well under way. At night they roost up in lofty trees, and at early dawn the jungle resounds with the loud ugly screaming *may-awe* calls of the cocks which seem such a sorry anticlimax to their gorgeous appearance. The food consists mainly of grain, tubers, and vegetable shoots, but the bird is omnivorous and will readily take insects, lizards, and small snakes as well. Where protected by the villagers peafowl enter the cultivators' fields with impunity and often do considerable damage to newly sown groundnut and cereal crops. The nest is a shallow scrape in the ground lined with sticks and leaves, usually well concealed in dense undergrowth. The normal clutch is of 3 to 5 eggs, pale cream to café-au-lait in colour.

The Order GRUIFORMES is represented in the Indian sub-continent by a number of families of which GRUIDAE (Cranes), RALLIDAE (Rails) and OTIDIDAE (Bustards) are significant. The Cranes are typified by the **Saras Crane** (*Grus antigone*)—PLATE 32 —Hindi: *Sārās*. This is a large grey bird of the size of a vulture and as tall as a man. It has long bare red legs, and naked red head and upper neck. The bird is met with mostly in pairs stalking about in cultivation and marshland, seasonally accompanied by one or two young. Flocks are rare, though gatherings of a hundred birds or more are not unknown. They pair for life and their marital devotion has become legendary in folk-lore, earning for them a degree of popular sentiment amounting almost to sanctity. They are un-molested by the country folk and have thus become tame and confiding everywhere in sharp contrast with their migratory relations which are zealously hunted for the excellence of their flesh and are therefore amongst the wariest and most wide awake of the game

4

birds. Saras rise off the ground heavily and with some effort, but when properly launched their flight is swift and powerful attained by seemingly slow rhythmical strokes of the great wings—neck extended, legs trailing behind. They have loud, sonorous, far-reaching trumpet-like calls uttered on the ground as well as in flight. During the breeding season, and sometimes also otherwise, the pair indulges in spectacular but somewhat ludicrous dancing displays and caperings—bowing to each other, spreading out their wings, and prancing and leaping wildly in the air. Their diet consists of grain, tubers, shoots and other vegetable matter as well as insects, molluscs, frogs, reptiles, and occasionally fish. Having the free run of the fields they sometimes do considerable local damage with impunity to newly sown groundnut and cereal crops. The nest of the Saras is a huge mass of reeds, rushes and straw built on the ground in the middle of a flooded paddy field or on a grassy bund or islet in a swamp. The eggs, normally 2, are pale greenish- or pinkish white in colour, sometimes spotted and blotched with brown or purple.

Two other grey cranes visit the Indian subcontinent in vast numbers during winter. The smaller of the two is the **Demoiselle** (*Anthropoides virgo*)—Hindi: *Kărkără* or *Koonj*—distinguished by its feathered head with glistening white ear-tufts, and black neck and breast. The other is the *Kŭlăng* or **Common Crane** (*Grus grus*) which has a naked black crown and a distinctive red patch across the nape.

The Rails (family RALLIDAE) are skulking marsh-haunting birds of small to moderate size, with stubby tails, rounded wings, and longish bare legs and toes. A familiar example is the **Whitebreasted Waterhen** (*Amaurornis phoenicurus*)—PLATE 33—Hindi: *Jăl mŭrghi* or *Dauk*. It is a common slaty grey stub-tailed, bare-legged marsh bird of the size of the Grey Partridge, with prominent white face and breast, and bright rusty red under the cocked-up tail. The Whitebreasted Waterhen is inseparable from the neighbourhood of water and usually met with singly or in pairs in or near reedbeds and thickets on the edge of jheels and village ponds. In the monsoon, when ditches fill and rain-puddles form, it strays further afield and may commonly be seen along roadside hedges and on the grassy shoulders of country roads. As it saunters along circumspectly, or skulks its way through the hedges and undergrowth, its stumpy erect tail is constantly jerked up displaying prominently the red underneath. It is usually a shy bird and resents observation, betaking itself to cover on the least suspicion, but where unmolested soon becomes confiding, entering gardens and moving about on the lawns and along hedgerows with charming unconcern. Its food consists of insects, molluscs, worms and seeds and other vegetable matter. The bird is silent except in the rainy season when it is breeding. The males then become very pugnacious and noisy, clambering up into the top or centre of a leafy bush and giving vent to their loud unbirdlike calls and caterwauling. The calls begin with raucous grunts, croaks, and chuckles—a metallic *krr-kwwaak-kwaak, krr-kwaak-kwaak*, etc.—suggestive of a bear in agony—and settle down to a monotonous *kook-kook-kook* and so on, rather like a Coppersmith barbet's but higher in key and faster in tempo. In the distance these calls are clearly mistakable for the 'pooking' of an oil-engined flour mill, now such an ubiquitous sign of modernity on our rural countryside! The calling is kept up for 15 minutes or more at a stretch and continues intermittently throughout the day, especially if cloudy, and all through the night. The nest of this waterhen is a shallow cup-shaped pad of twigs and creeper-stems placed on the ground in tangled growth, or 5 ft. or so up in a thick bush near water. The eggs—6 or 7—are cream or pinkish white in colour, streaked and blotched with reddish brown.

A handsome but rather clumsy member of the rail family is the **Purple Moorhen** (*Porphyrio porphyrio*)—PLATE 34—Hindi: *Kaim, Kharim* or *Kalim*. It is about the size of a village hen, purplish blue with long bare red legs and toes. The bald red forehead (frontal shield) continued back from the short heavy red bill, and the white patch under the stumpy tail, conspicuous when flicked up at each step, are leading clues to its identity. The bird is found gregariously among swampy reedbeds where scattered parties spend their time stalking or skulking in the reeds in search of food or clambering awkwardly up the stems in hand-over-hand fashion. They saunter over the floating weeds and lotus leaves, constantly flicking their tails in the characteristic rail manner. The birds run to cover when disturbed, but are averse to flying unless compelled. The flight appears laboured and feeble with the long ungainly red legs dangling behind, but they can travel quite fast when well under way. Their diet is mainly shoots of paddy and marsh plants and the birds are locally destructive to rice crops more by trampling down the plants with their large feet than by the grain they actually eat. Insects and snails are also taken. They have a variety of hooting, cackling and harsh notes which may be heard at all times of the day—especially in cloudy weather—emanating from within their native reedbeds. The birds are particularly noisy during their breeding season when the male goes through a ludicrous courtship display, holding water weeds in his bill and facing and bowing to his mate to the accompaniment of loud chuckles. The Purple Moorhen is not considered a 'game bird' by sophisticated sportsmen, but is highly prized as a delicacy by country folk and greatly persecuted by local shikaris. The nest is a large pad of interwoven rushes or paddy leaves placed on matted water plants within flooded reedbeds. The normal clutch consists of 3 to 7 eggs, creamy to reddish buff in colour, blotched and spotted with reddish brown.

Of our Bustards (family OTIDIDAE), perhaps the most interesting and significant species is the **Great Indian Bustard** (*Choriotis nigriceps*)—PLATE 35—Hindi: *Tūqdār* or *Hūknā*. It is a large ground bird of about the size of a vulture, standing about 3 feet to the top of its head and weighing anything up to 30 pounds. Its appearance is suggestive of a miniature ostrich, and the horizontal carriage of the body, at right angles to the stout bare legs, is characteristic. The upper plumage is deep buff, finely vermiculated with black; the underparts are white with a broad black gorget across the lower breast. The white neck, black crown, and a large whitish patch near the tip of the broad wings, conspicuous in flight, are other arresting features. The female is smaller. The *Tūqdār* is met with sporadically as a solitary bird or in twos and threes loosely together, but scattered droves of 25 to 30 have been recorded in the past. Its favourite haunts are open semi-desert plains and sparse grassland interspersed with light scrub jungle and cultivation. The bird is excessively shy and wary and can seldom be approached except by subterfuge such as in a harmless-looking bullock cart or on or behind a camel. Unfortunately the birds are also foolishly unsuspicious of poachers' Jeeps which are very largely responsible for bringing about the near extinction of the species in recent years despite the statutory total ban on its killing. The bustard is heavy in the take-off, but once air-borne flies strongly with steady rhythmical wing beats, never at any great height, but often sustained for several kilometres at a stretch. Its food consists principally of locusts, grasshoppers, beetles, grain, and tender shoots of various crop plants. Lizards, small snakes, and centipedes are also eaten. The usual alarm note is a bark or bellow, something like *hook*. The cock is polygynous and displays struttingly before his harem, rather in the style of a turkey-cock, to the accompaniment of a deep moaning call. The single egg—rarely 2—is laid in a shallow depression at the base of some bush in sparsely scrubbed country. It is drab or pale olive-brown in colour, faintly blotched with deep brown.

The Order CHARADRIIFORMES is a large and heterogeneous conglomeration of 13 families of water- or waterside birds, well represented in the Indian subcontinent by resident as well as migratory forms. One of these families is JAÇANIDAE—Jaçanas or Lilytrotters, of which we have two species. The **Bronzewinged Jaçana** (*Metopidius indicus*)—PLATE 36—is a leggy swamp bird as big as the Grey Partridge and something like a moorhen in general aspect. It has glossy black head, neck, and breast, metallic greenish bronze back and wings, and chestnut-red stub tail. The broad white stripe from behind eye to the nape is conspicuous and tell-tale even when the bird is partly hidden from view. Immature birds are chiefly whitish, rufous, and brown. The enormously elongated spidery toes are a feature of all jaçanas and adapt them admirably for a life on vegetation-covered tanks and jheels, the spreading toes helping to distribute the weight and enabling the birds to trip lightly over the tangles of floating leaves and stems in search of aquatic insects and molluscs, and the seeds and roots of water plants, and other vegetable matter that constitute their diet. Where unmolested the birds become tame and unafraid. They may commonly be seen on village tanks in unconcerned proximity of the chattering womenfolk trooping down with their water pots or of the dhobi noisily battering his washing on the accustomed stone. Both our species are good divers and can also swim when occasion demands. But their flight is feeble, with rapidly beating wings, neck extended and the cumbrous feet dangling awkwardly behind. The call of the Bronzewinged Jaçana is a shrill wheezing pipe *seek-seek-seek* etc., and the birds become particularly noisy and bellicose during the breeding season. They also utter a short harsh grunt.

Our other common resident jaçana is the **Pheasant-tailed** (*Hydrophasianus chirurgus*) of similar habits and habitat, the two species being frequently found together on the same ponds. It is distinguished by its striking white and chocolate-brown coloration and long, pointed, sickle shaped 'pheasant' tail.

In both species the female is polyandrous. She mates with a male, lays eggs and leaves them to be hatched, and the young to be reared, entirely by him. She has several successive husbands in this way. The nest is a skimpy pad of twisted weed-stems, placed on floating *singara* or water hyacinth leaves. The eggs of the Bronzewinged—normally 4—are a handsome bronze-brown in colour with an irregular network of blackish scrawls and squiggles; those of the Pheasant-tailed are glossy greenish bronze or rufous-brown, without any markings.

Of the family CHARADRIIDAE—Plovers, Sandpipers, etc.—many forms are resident and others visit us during winter mainly from northern lands. The **Redwattled Lapwing** (*Vanellus indicus*)—

PLATE 37—Hindi: *Titeeri* or *Titūri* is the commonest and most familiar of our resident plovers. It is the size of the Grey Partridge, bronze-brown above, white below, with black breast, head and neck, and a crimson fleshy wattle in front of each eye. A broad white band from behind the eyes runs down the sides of the neck to meet the white underparts. Pairs or small scattered parties of 3 or 4 haunt open country, ploughed fields, and grazing grounds, usually damp and preferably with a pond or puddle nearby. They spend their time running about in short spurts, picking up titbits in the typical manner of plovers, bill pointed steeply to the ground, and are quite as active and wide-awake at night as during daytime. They maintain an uncanny vigil and any suspicious intruder in their domains, whether man or carnivore, is greeted with frantic calls and agitated behaviour. The call is the all too well known *Did-ye-do-it* ? or *Pity-to-do-it* uttered placidly or frantically, just once or twice or repeatedly, depending upon the occasion and the provocation. When the nest or young are threatened the agitated parents fly around close overhead screaming hysterically and diving repeatedly at the intruder making as if to strike. The food consists of insects, grubs, and molluscs. The normal flight is slow, attained by deliberate flaps of the wings. The bird alights after a short distance, usually running a few steps on touching down. The nest of the Redwattled Lapwing is merely an unlined depression or scrape in the ground, sometimes margined with pebbles. Drying-up beds of village tanks, and sunbaked fallow fields are favoured sites. Some unusual sites have occasionally been reported such as the flat concrete roof of a bungalow and the stone metal between the rails on a regularly used railway siding. The eggs—normally 3 or 4—are some shade of grey-brown, blotched with blackish. They, as well as the newly hatched downy chicks, are perfect examples of natural camouflage and can be completely invisible even when almost under the observer's nose

The **Common Sandpiper** (*Tringa hypoleucos*)—PLATE 38—is one of the large group of bare-legged, slender-billed marsh and waterside birds collectively known as 'snippets' in popular language.

It is about the size of a quail, greyish olive-brown above, white below, with the sides of the breast pale dusky and a few dark streaks on the foreneck. In flight the *brown* rump and *brown* tail (excepting only the white outer feathers), and a white wing-bar distinguish it from the equally common Wood Sandpiper. The Common Sandpiper is one of our earliest immigrants and among the last to leave for its northern breeding grounds, the nearest of which lie in Kashmir and Garhwal. Some non-breeding individuals stay behind in the plains all the year. Unlike the Wood Sandpiper this species seldom collects in flocks. Single birds are usually seen running about tirelessly at the water's edge, wagging the tail end of the body violently and 'pumping' its head and neck from time to time. When disturbed it flies off with characteristic stiff rapidly vibrating wing strokes close over the water uttering a shrill piping *tee-tee-tee*. A pretty, long-drawn piping song, *wheeit wheeit* repeated several times, is commonly heard when the bird is completely at its ease. Individuals are very parochial, keeping to the same feeding territory day after day. The diet, like that of other sandpipers, consists of insects, worms, tiny molluscs, etc. picked up at the water's edge. The nest is a slight depression lined with leaves, on a shinglebank or islet in a swirling stream. The eggs—normally 4—are yellowish buff or stone colour, blotched and speckled with reddish brown.

The **Wood** or **Spotted Sandpiper** (*Tringa glareola*), also a common winter visitor from as far north as Siberia, is more gregarious and readily distinguished in flight by its *white* rump and *white* tail, and by the shrill *chiff-chiff-chiff-chiff* it utters when flying off.

The **Little Ringed Plover** (*Charadrius dubius*)—PLATE 39—Hindi: *Zirrea* or *Merwā* is slightly smaller than the quail. It is a typical plover, sandy brown above, white below, with thick round head, bare slender legs, and short, stout pigeon-like bill. It has a white forehead and black forecrown, ear-coverts, and round the eyes, and a complete black band round the neck separating the white hindcollar from the brown back. Absence of a white wing-bar in flight distinguishes it from the confusingly similar **Kentish Plover** (*C. alexandrinus*). The birds keep in pairs or small scattered flocks on damp tank margins, river banks, and tidal mudflats. They run along the ground in spurts with short quick mincing steps, stopping abruptly every now and again to pick up some titbit with the peculiar steeply tilting movement characteristic of the plovers. They have a curious habit, when feeding on soft mud, of drumming with their toes in a rapid vibratory motion in order to dislodge insects, sandhoppers, and tiny crabs lurking in burrows and unevennesses. These constitute their normal food. In their normal environment their coloration blends with the surroundings in a remarkable way making the birds difficult to spot so long as they remain motionless. Although these little plovers keep scattered while feeding, yet no sooner does one take alarm and rise than the rest will promptly follow suit, all flying off in a compact body at great speed, turning, twisting, and banking together, their white undersides flashing in unison from time to time. The flight, attained by rapid strokes of the pointed wings, is swift but seldom more than 4 or 5 metres above the ground. The eggs—almost invariably 4—are laid among the shingle on dry sandbanks in a river bed. They are of the typical peg-top shape of plovers' eggs, buffish stone to greenish grey in colour with scrawls and spots of dark brown and purplish. They harmonize perfectly with their surroundings and are difficult to spot even when their position has been carefully marked down from a distance.

The family BURHINIDAE is represented by the **Stone Curlew** or **Goggle-eyed Plover** (*Burhinus oedicnemus*)—PLATE 40—Hindi: *Kărwānăk* or *Bărsiri*. It is a brown-streaked plover-like ground bird, larger and more leggy than the Grey Partridge, with thick round head, bare yellow 'thick-kneed' legs, and large yellow 'goggle' eyes. In flight two narrow white bars on the upper side of the wing and a broad white patch near the tips of the black primaries give leading clues to its identity. The Stone Curlew frequents open scrub and bush country, ploughed and fallow land, and dry shingle beds in rivers. It is occasionally found in light deciduous jungle and shady mango topes in the neighbourhood of villages. Pairs or parties of 4 or 5 is the rule. As the large eyes suggest, the bird is chiefly crepuscular and nocturnal, and sluggish during daytime. When suspicious or alarmed it scuttles away surreptitiously with short quick steps, head ducked and neck craned horizontally in line with the body. The bird then squats and freezes at the foot of a bush or stone, body pressed to the ground, neck resting extended in front, and the staring eye following the movements of the intruder. In this position its coloration and contours blend with the surroundings in an astonishing way, and render the bird completely invisible even at short range. Its food consists mainly of insects, worms, slugs, small reptiles, etc., with which a quantity of grit is commonly swallowed. The call of the stone curlew, normally heard at dusk and dawn, and also throughout moonlit nights, is a series of sharp clear whistling screams *pick, pick, pick, pick...pick-wick, pick-wick, pick-wick* (accent on the second syllable). Although the calls themselves are familiar to many, they are seldom recognized as produced by this species. The nest is a simple scrape at the base of a bush or grass-tussock on stony ground, in a dry river bed, mango grove, or open scrub country. The eggs—usually 2—are pale buff to olive-green in colour, boldly blotched with brownish or purplish and, like their layer, remarkably obliterative in their stony environment.

In keeping with our extensive coastline the family LARIDAE— Gulls and Terns—is well represented by resident as well as migratory forms.

Gulls differ from terns superficially in being rather heavier-built with broader and less pointed wings. One of our commonest species is the **Brownheaded Gull** (*Larus brunnicephalus*)—PLATE 41— Hindi: *Dhomra*. It is slightly larger than the Jungle Crow, grey above white below, with a dark coffee-brown head in summer. In winter, whilst with us, the head is greyish white, sometimes with a crescent-shaped vertical black mark behind the ear. It may be distinguished from the equally common but somewhat smaller **Blackheaded Gull** (*L. ridibundus*) by the prominent white patch or 'mirror' near the tip of the black first primary quill; in the Blackheaded species the first wing quill is white with black edges and tip. Young birds of both species have a black bar near the tip of the white tail. Both are often found together on the seacoast; less commonly inland. These gulls arrive in India in September-October to spend the winter on our coasts and inland waters, and are mostly gone again by the end of April. They frequent harbours, docks, and coastal fishing villages, flying around ships at anchor and escorting outgoing and incoming vessels for the sake of the kitchen scraps and garbage thrown overboard. Their food here consists chiefly of this and of dead fish cast out by fishing boats for which they have to compete with the Pariah and Brahminy Kites. The birds swoop down to the water and pick up the floating titbits with their bills, often alighting on the surface alongside and riding the wavelets buoyantly like ducks. In inland localities they also eat insects, grubs, and some vegetable matter. The Brownheaded Gull has a number of loud raucous calls, the one most commonly heard being a querulous scream *keeah*, rather like a raven's.

Within Indian limits this gull breeds only on the high altitude lakes in Ladakh. It nests in colonies laying its eggs on simple pads of water-weeds scraped together on semi-floating grassy islets in bogs. The full clutch consists of 2 or 3 eggs, variably coloured greenish white to creamy buff, with large blotches and spots and squiggly lines of dark or reddish brown.

A good example of terns is the **Indian Whiskered Tern** (*Chlidonias hybrida*)—PLATE 42—Hindi: *Tehāri, Koorri* (all terns), a slender graceful silvery grey and white bird about the size of a pigeon, but considerably slimmer. It belongs to the group known as 'marsh terns', characterized by a tail which is only slightly forked (almost square-cut). The bill is red or blackish red, and when at rest the tips of the closed wings project beyond the tail. In summer dress (breeding) both sexes don a black cap, and the belly also becomes conspicuously black. The Whiskered Tern is usually seen over marshland, inundated paddy fields or coastal mudflats flying back and forth airily and elegantly on its long narrow wings, bill and eye intently directed below as it scans the water or mud for its prey. From time to time the bird swoops down at a tangent to whisk off a sand crab or insect or tadpole or small fish from the surface. Off shore, the birds attend on the fishing boats returning with the catch for any sprats and fingerlings that may be cast over-board. Though possessing webbed feet and capable of swimming, terns hardly ever alight on the water as gulls do. They spend most of their time in the air or resting on the shore on their ridiculously short legs. The calls, uttered in flight, are a sharp harsh *creeak*, *creeak* reminiscent in the distance of the harsh churring notes of a shrike.

Another common tern is the **River Tern** (*Sterna aurantia*) which keeps more to rivers than to marshes. It is also grey and white with a brown-speckled cap but somewhat larger, with a *yellow* bill, and longer more deeply forked swallow tail. In breeding dress the cap turns jet black but the underparts remain white.

The Whiskered Tern breeds in northern India and Kashmir. The nest is a skimpy circular pad of reeds and rushes placed on half-submerged floating tangles of *singāra* and similar plants in a lake or swamp. The normal clutch is of 2 or 3 eggs, variable in colour from greenish to bluish or even brownish. They are spotted, blotched and streaked with dark brown or purplish brown.

The Order COLUMBIFORMES is represented in our area by the Sandgrouse (family PTEROCLIDAE), and the Pigeons and Doves (COLUMBIDAE). Both the families include many species that are highly prized as sporting birds and for the table. They are characterized, among other things, by their method of drinking water which consists, not like the domestic hen of dipping the bill to suck and raising the head to swallow, but like a horse—a continuous uninterrupted sucking with the bill kept immersed.

Sandgrouse are superficially pigeon-like birds, with dense, cryptically coloured brownish plumage. They have short necks, very short legs, and tapering tails with elongated pin-pointed central feathers in many species. They inhabit open semi-desert areas and fallow cultivation in flocks, often of considerable size, and have the well known habit of resorting to favourite drinking places at fixed hours. The **Common Sandgrouse** (*Pterocles exustus*)—PLATE 43—Hindi: *Bhăt teetăr*, is a typical example. It is somewhat smaller than a pigeon, yellowish sandy brown and pin-tailed, with a narrow black band across the breast and brownish black belly. The cheeks, chin, and throat are dully yellow. The female is streaked, spotted and barred all over excepting the chin. She also has the black band across the breast. In overhead flight the pointed wings and tail, and the characteristic double note then uttered, proclaim its identity. The birds keep in flocks of a dozen or more on dry fallow land. Their general coloration is remarkably obliterative rendering the squatting birds completely invisible on the bare ground they frequent. Though often keeping considerable distances from water, the flocks flight regularly to quench their thirst in the morning and evening converging on a favourite jheel or tank at the appointed hour from every direction. The birds give excellent sport with the gun as they fly to and from their drinking places. The flight is strong and very swift, accompanied by the distinctive penetrating double note *kut-ro* clearly heard as the birds are passing overhead often long before they actually come into view. The food of sandgrouse consists of grass- and weed seeds, grain and shoots gleaned on the ground, along with which a great deal of grit is swallowed. They lay their eggs on the bare soil, sometimes in a shallow unlined scrape. The normal clutch is of 3 eggs, pale greyish or yellowish stone in colour, spattered with numerous specks and spots of brown. The chicks are covered with protectively coloured down and are able to run about as soon as hatched. The male parent conveys water to them by soaking his belly feathers while wading in to drink, with which he subsequently suckles the chicks.

Just as in the case of duck and teal, there is no real difference between pigeons and doves; pigeons are merely large doves, and doves small pigeons. There is one group of pigeons that is entirely frugivorous and to it belong the green pigeons known in Hindi as *Häriäl*. Of the many species found in the subcontinent, the commonest is the **Common Green Pigeon** (*Treron phoenicoptera*)— PLATE 44. It is a stocky bird of the size of the domestic blue pigeon, yellow, olive-green and ashy grey, with a lilac patch on the wing-shoulders—less pronounced in the female—and a conspicuous yellow bar across the blackish wings. The *yellow* (not red) legs distinguish this species from all other Indian green pigeons. It is met with in flocks in open wooded country as well as forest, and is commonly found in the vicinity of town and villages, even entering city gardens where there are suitable fruiting trees to attract it. It is gregarious and almost exclusively arboreal, only rarely descending to the ground. The birds clamber deftly among the fruit-laden twigs, often clinging upside down and lunging out in that position to pluck a banyan or peepal fig just out of reach. When suspicious of danger they 'freeze', and so perfectly does their plumage blend with the surrounding green leaves that in spite of their large size they become completely invisible until some slight movement here and another there gives them away. The unsuspected numbers that will flutter out of a large fig-laden banyan tree when a gun is fired is often quite bewildering. The flocks spend the day doing the rounds of fruiting trees, resting on the topmost branches between the intervals of gorging. The birds are regularly seen sunning themselves with fluffed-out plumage on the tops of leafless trees in the early mornings and at sunset. Their flight is swift, strong, and direct, and attended by a peculiar metallic clapping of the wings. Green pigeons live almost entirely on fruit, the various species of wild fig (*Ficus*) forming the bulk. They have very pleasant soft and mellow whistling calls ranging up and down the scale and with a peculiar human quality. The nest is a skimpy platform of twigs like a dove's, concealed in the foliage of moderate sized trees. Characteristically of the pigeon family, the eggs invariably number 2, and are white and glossy.

The **Blue Rock Pigeon** (*Columba livia*)—PLATE 45—Hindi:

Kăbūtăr, is our well known slaty grey bird with glistening metallic green, purple, and magenta sheen on the neck and upper breast, two dark bars on the wings, and a broader one across the end of the tail. It ranks with the crow and the house sparrow as one of our most familiar birds. The wild form, which is the ancestor of all our divergent fancy domestic breeds, affects open country with cliffs and rocky hills and avoids heavy forest. In most localities, however, it has freely interbred with domestic stock and degenerated into a confirmed commensal of man. Almost every Indian town has its resident pigeon population. The birds become thoroughly inured to the din and bustle of the most congested bazars and lead a life of pampered indolence, roosting and nesting on or in the buildings. Warehouse and factory sheds, mosques, and railway stations and goods yards are particularly favoured haunts, and here they become an unmitigated nuisance for the filthy mess they make. In the wild state colonies of pigeons are commonly found occupying holes in shafts of old wells, crumbling buildings, ancient hill forts, and ledges and fissures of rock scarps whence they flight back and forth to glean in newly sown or harvested fields of cereals, pulses and groundnuts, etc. The call notes are well known: a deep *gootr-goo*, *gootr-goo* by the male with puffed-out throat, usually as he bows to his mate and slowly turns round and round in front of her. The nest is a sketchy pad of twigs and straw. The eggs, as typical of the family, are 2 in number and unmarked white.

The **Spotted Dove** (*Streptopelia chinensis*)—PLATE 46 (top)—Hindi: *Chitrōkā fākhta* or *Perki*, is between the myna and the pigeon in size. It is a small slim pigeon with conspicuous white-spotted pinkish brown and grey upper parts, with a white-speckled black 'chessboard' on the hindneck. It is met with in pairs and small parties in openly wooded, well-watered country and cultivation, gleaning on dusty paths and in stubble fields, etc. Where unmolested, the birds become very tame, entering gardens and even nesting on rafters of bungalow verandahs unperturbed by the comings and goings of the inmates. Its call is an oft-repeated pleasant though rather mournful *kroo-krūk-krūk-kroo*...*kroo-kroo-kroo*, the number of *kroos* varying from 3 to 6. The nest is of the customary type—a sketchy and flimsy pad of a few thin twigs in a shrub, or on a ledge or cornice in a bungalow. The usual 2 white eggs form the clutch.

Another dove slightly larger than a myna, is the **Red Turtle Dove** (*Streptopelia tranquebarica*)—PLATE 46 (bottom)—Hindi: *Serōti fākhtā, Gīrwi fākhtā* or *Itwa*. The female differs from the male (illustrated) in having the mantle pale brownish grey instead of bright pinkish brick-red. She looks a smaller edition of the Ring Dove (Hindi: *Dhōr fākhtā*). The Red Turtle Dove is met with in small numbers in open cultivated country, also in semi-desert. Though not uncommon, it is perhaps the least abundant of the doves on our countryside and, unlike the other species, seldom found in close association with man. Its call is a somewhat harsh rolling *groo-gūrr-goo, groo-gūrr-goo*—quickly repeated several times. Its nest is the usual sketchy dove platform or pad of twigs, built in a branch 10 to 20 ft. above the ground. The normal clutch of 2 white eggs can usually be seen through the flimsy fabric of the nest from below.

The Order PSITTACIFORMES contains a single family, PSITTACIDAE—Parrots. These birds are characterized by short, stout and strongly hooked bills, short legs, and climbing or zygodactyl feet, *i.e.* with two toes pointing in front and two behind. They are all predominantly green plumaged ornamental birds, but highly destructive to crops and orchard fruit and possessing few redeeming qualities from the economic point of view. Our commonest species is the **Roseringed Parakeet** (*Psittacula krameri*)—PLATE 47—Hindi: *Tōtā* or *Lybār tōtā*, slightly larger than a myna and with a long pointed tail. It is a grass-green parakeet with the typical short stout deeply hooked red bill, and a black-and-rosepink collar. The female lacks the collar, but otherwise is like the male. The Roseringed Parakeet also ranks with the crow, sparrow, myna and pigeon amongst our commonest and most familiar birds.

WHITEBREASTED WATERHEN
(*Amaurornis phoenicurus*)
(*see* page 50)

PLATE 34
PURPLE MOORHEN
(*Porphyrio porphyrio*)
(*seee* page 51)

PLATE 35
GREAT INDIAN BUSTARD
(Choriotis nigriceps)
(see page 52)

0   25 CM   H·M

PLATE 36
BRONZEWINGED JAÇANA
(*Metopidius indicus*)
(*see* page 53)

PLATE 37
REDWATTLED LAPWING
(Vanellus indicus)
(see page 54)

PLATE 38
COMMON SANDPIPER
(*Tringa hypoleucos*)
(*see* page 55)

PLATE 40
STONE CURLEW or GOGGLE-EYED PLOVER
(*Burhinus oedicnemus*)
(*see* page 57)

PLATE 41
BROWNHEADED GULL
(*Larus brunnicephalus*)
(*see* page 58)

PLATE 42
INDIAN WHISKERED TERN
(*Chlidonias hybrida*)
(in breeding plumage)
(*see* page 59)

PLATE 43
COMMON SANDGROUSE
(Pterocles exustus)
(*see* page 61)

PLATE 44
COMMON GREEN PIGEON
(*Treron phoenicoptera*)
(*see* page 62)

PLATE 45
BLUE ROCK PIGEON
(*Columba livia*)
(*see* page 62)

PLATE 46
SPOTTED DOVE (top)
(*Streptopelia chinensis*)

RED TURTLE DOVE (bottom)
(*Streptopelia tranquebarica*)
(*see* pages 63-4)

PLATE 47
ROSERINGED PARAKEET
(*Psittacula krameri*)
(*see* page 64)

PLATE 48
KOEL
(*Eudynamys scolopacea*)
(*see* page 66)

It bands itself into very large flocks or rabbles in cultivated and urban areas where food is plentiful, and is a serious pest to the farmer and fruit grower causing enormous depredations to his standing crops and ripening orchard fruit, gnawing at and wasting far more than it actually eats. It is a common sight at roadside railway stations to see swarms of parakeets clinging to sacks of grain and groundnuts awaiting transport, calmly biting into them and helping themselves to the contents. The parakeets have common roosts in groves of trees often within the precincts of noisy cities, to which battalion after battalion flies noisily every evening from long distances after marauding on the surrounding country-side. Their familiar sharp screaming calls *keeak, keeak, keeak,* are uttered both while at rest and on the wing. This species as well as the Large Parakeet, known *Rāi tōtā* or *Hirāmǎn tōtā,* are popular cage birds and can be taught to repeat a few words and sentences rather indistinctly, and to perform various table-top tricks such as muzzle-loading with gunpowder and firing off a toy cannon. The eggs—4 to 6, pure white roundish ovals—are laid in old barbet- or woodpecker holes or in holes in cliffs or walls of inhabited houses, several pairs often nesting colonially. The **Large Indian** or **Alexandrine Parakeet** (*Psittacula eupatria*) is distinguished by its larger size, more massive bill, and a conspicuous maroon patch on the shoulder of the male. The female lacks the mároon patch as well as the black-and-pink collar. It is found in more wooded, less urban localities. Large numbers of nestlings of both species are brought for sale in bird markets.

The Order CUCULIFORMES includes the cuckoos, which have a practically worldwide distribution. Many of the Old World species are notorious for their habit of brood parasitism, *i.e.* laying their eggs in the nests of other birds and foisting on them the responsibility of hatching them and rearing the young. Classical of the parasitic cuckoos is the European Cuckoo (*Cuculus canorus*) which extends into Kashmir and the western Himalayas and has a resident race in Assam. But the commonest example of this group in the subcontinent is the **Koel** (*Eudynamys scolopacea*)—PLATE 48— Hindi: *Koel* or *Kōkilā*. It is about the size of a crow but slenderer and with a longer tail. The male is glistening metallic black all over, with a striking yellowish green bill and crimson or blood-red eyes. The female is brown, spotted and barred with white. The Koel, though actually a very common and widespread bird of gardens and groves, is perhaps better known by its voice than by its appearance. It is entirely arboreal and never descends to the ground. During winter it is silent and thus often overlooked and presumed to have migrated. But with the approach of summer and its breeding time, it regains its voice and becomes extremely noisy. In the hot season the loud, shrill, crescendo calls of the male— *kūoo-kūoo-kūoo*—resound on the countryside throughout the day and far into the night. They begin with a low *kūoo* and rise higher and higher in scale with each successive *kūoo* until, at the seventh or eighth, they reach frantic pitch and break off abruptly. The bird soon commences it all over again, and so on and on *ad nauseam*. The Koel's 'song' has been much lauded in romantic Hindi poetry and song, and in small doses it is indeed quite pleasant to hear. But it is apt to become monotonous and even nerve-racking by its incessant shrieking repetition, and it is not without reason that the bird is sometimes miscalled the Brainfever Bird which is in reality the Hawk-Cuckoo or *Papeeha*. The female Koel has no song. She only utters a shrill *kik-kik-kik* as she dashes from tree to tree or hops among the branches. The food consists chiefly of banyan and peepal figs, various berries, and hairy caterpillars. The laying season corresponds with that of its normal hosts the House and Jungle Crows. Like other parasitic cuckoos the Koel builds no nest of its own but deposits its eggs in crows' nests leaving them to be hatched, and the young to be reared, by the foster parents. The eggs, which may be distributed over several crows' nests, are pale greyish green, speckled and blotched with reddish brown. They closely resemble crows' eggs but are smaller.

An example of the so-called non-parasitic cuckoos, *i.e.* those

that build nests and take care of their own family affairs is the
Crow-Pheasant or **Coucal** (*Centropus sinensis*)—PLATE 49—Hindi:
Măhōkā or *kūkā*, about the size of a Jungle Crow. It is a clumsy but
strikingly coloured bird, glossy black with chestnut wings and long,
broad, graduated black tail. The Crow-Pheasant is a dweller
of open scrub country abounding in bushes and small trees, and
interspersed with patches of tall grass land and cultivation. It is
often found in the neighbourhood of human habitation and freely
enters gardens. It is largely a terrestrial or ground-living species
and spends its time walking about purposively through the undergrowth in search of food, tail almost trailing on the ground and
wings frequently snapped open and shut to stampede lurking
insects. In its quest the bird also clambers among the bushes and hops
with agility from branch to branch in trees. Its call is a deep resonant
ook repeated at slow but regular intervals, especially during the
hot weather, and can be heard a long way off. A variant of this
call is a quick-repeated rather musical *coop-coop-coop-coop* in
runs of 6 or 7 and up to 20, repeated at the rate of 2 or 3 *coops* per
second. The calling is promptly joined in by another bird in the
distance and then continued as an irregular duet. The bird also
produces a medley of harsh croaks and gurgling chuckles, some
distinctly weird. In the breeding season the male goes through
a fantastic display before his mate, fanning and cocking his tail
over the back and strutting in front of her with wings drooping.
The crow-pheasant's flight is feeble and laboured, and only for short
distances. Its food consists of grasshoppers and other large insects
and caterpillars, field mice, lizards, small snakes, etc. The bird
is highly destructive to the eggs and nestlings of small birds and
hunts for them methodically on the ground and amongst shrubbery.
The flesh of the Coucal is much esteemed by quacks as a remedy
for various bronchial ailments. The bird belongs to the group of
non-parasitic cuckoos and, unlike the Koel, raises its own family.
The nest is a large untidy globular mass of leaves and twigs with
a side entrance, placed fairly low down in a thorny tree. The eggs
—3 or 4—are white, unmarked and with a chalky surface.

The Order STRIGIFORMES—Owls—is represented by two families namely TYTONINAE (Barn Owl) and STRIGIDAE (True Owls). The former is characterized by its pinched monkey-like facial disc as typified by our familiar Barn Owl (*Tyto alba*) of almost worldwide distribution. The True Owls have large round heads and large round forwardly directed staring eyes. Some species possess erectile horn-like feather-tufts above the eyes. One of our commonest species is the **Spotted Owlet** (*Athene brama*)—PLATE 50— Hindi: *Khūsăttia* or *Chūghăd*, about the size of a myna but plumper. It is a squat, white-spotted greyish brown little owl with typical large round head and forwardly directed unblinking eyes. It affects open plains and foothills country, and is usually abundant and thoroughly at home in the midst of human habitations. Ancient mango, banyan, and suchlike trees with holes and fissures usually harbour a pair or two, and one has but to tap on the trunk to bring forth an enquiring little face to the entrance, or to dislodge a pair sitting huddled together on some secluded bough. The birds fly out fussily to a neighbouring branch whence they bob and stare un-blinkingly at the intruder in clownish fashion, sometimes screwing the head completely round in the process. They are largely crepus-cular and nocturnal, hiding during daytime and issuing forth at dusk. They may be seen in the twilight perched on fence posts, telegraph wires and the like, pouncing from time to time on beetles and grasshoppers crawling on the ground, or flying across noiselessly from one vantage point to another. Occasionally a bird will launch ungainly aerial sallies after winged termites as they emerge from the rain-sodden ground, or after beetles round a street lamp, seizing the insects in its claws, returning to the perch and tearing them to shreds by raising the foot to the bill like a parakeet. Sometimes a bird will hover clumsily like a kestrel to espy creeping prey. The food con-sists mainly of beetles and other insects, but lizards and baby mice and birds are also taken. These owlets are noisy birds and have a variety of harsh chattering, squabbling, and chuckling notes, two individuals frequently combining in a discordant duet. The eggs, 3 or 4, are laid in hollows or holes in buildings—ruined or in occupation—sparsely lined with grass, feathers, etc. They are white roundish ovals.

The other commonly seen owl is the **Great Horned Owl** (*Bubo bubo*)—PLATE 51—Hindi: *Ghūghū*. This is about the size of a Pariah Kite but more robust. It is a large heavy dark brown owl streaked and mottled with tawny buff and black, with two conspicuous black ear-tufts or 'horns' above the head. It can be easily confused with the Brown Fish Owl (*Bubo zeylonicus*) but is less rufous and more yellow-brown generally. Moreover its legs are fully *feathered* and not bare as in the Fish Owl. The bird spends the day resting on the ground under shelter of a bush, or on some shady rocky projection in a ravine or river bank. It is by no means so completely crepuscular and nocturnal as the Fish Owl and may frequently be seen on the move during daytime. Normally the birds emerge from their daytime retreat at sunset with a deep, solemn, resounding call *Bu-bo* (2nd syllable much prolonged). This is not particularly loud but has a peculiar penetrating and far-reaching quality. They may then be seen perched on the top of some boulder or other exposed eminence whence they glide off effortlessly, sometimes for great distance, to their accustomed hunting grounds. In addition to the normal call they have a variety of weird growls and hisses expressive of excitement or emotion. The food of the Horned Owl consists mainly of small mammals, birds, lizards and other reptiles— also large insects and occasionally even fish and crabs. In agricultural areas field rats and mice form a considerable proportion of the diet. By maintaining a constant check on these fecund and destructive vermin they are of very great economic value to man and deserving of the strictest protection. The eggs—3 or 4—are laid without any nest on bare soil in natural recesses in earth banks, or in niches and on ledges of rock cliffs. Like all owls' eggs they are roundish ovals and creamy white in colour.

Of the two families which represent the Order CAPRIMULGI-FORMES in the Indian subcontinent, the one that chiefly concerns us is that of the Nightjars (CAPRIMULGIDAE). The Nightjars, or so-called 'Goat-suckers', are crepuscular or nocturnal birds with soft, concealing coloured plumage as in owls, very short and weak legs, and excessively wide gapes for catching flying insects on the wing in poor light. Stiff bristly feathers projecting from the gape further help to enlarge the catchment area. Several species of nightjars are found of which perhaps the commonest and most generally distributed is the **Indian Nightjar** (*Caprimulgus asiaticus*)—PLATE 52—Hindi: *Chhipăk* or *Dăb chiri*. It is about the size of a myna, soft-plumaged grey, brown, buff and fulvous, mottled and black-streaked, producing a complicated camouflaging pattern. White patches on its wings are conspicuous in flight. It is seen singly crouching on the ground in scrub country by day, hawking insects in the air at dusk or squatting on kutcha earth roads. Its food consists entirely of insects—beetles, moths, etc.—which are captured on the wing with the aid of the enormous gape. The flight of nightjars is peculiarly silent, moth-like and wandering, but the birds can turn and twist in the air in pursuit of prey, or to avoid obstacles, with amazing agility—now circling, now flapping, now sailing. When squatting on roads their large eyes gleam like rubies in the headlights of an oncoming car, and the birds are adept at dodging clear when within an ace of being run over. The call of this species is the familiar *chuk-chuk-chuk-chuk-r-r-r*, well likened to the sound of a stone gliding over a frozen pond. It is uttered after dusk and all through the night, from the ground or from the top of a tree-stump or mound. Two birds some distance apart will frequently engage in a duet, answering each other for considerable periods. The birds are noisy in the breeding season, particularly during moon-lit nights. No nest is made, the eggs—usually 2—being laid on the bare soil in thin bush jungle. They are long cylindrical ovals, pale pink to deep salmon in colour, spotted and blotched with reddish brown and inky purple.

The Order APODIFORMES includes the Swifts—slender stream-lined birds with long, narrow, bow-shaped wings especially adapted for extreme speed of flight. The birds spend most of the daylight

hours on the wing, dashing about hawking their insect prey—
midges, tiny bugs, and beetles—with the aid of their capacious
gapes. They have very short legs with all the four toes directed
forward, precluding the possibility of their perching, for example
on telegraph wires, like swallows. They can only cling to vertical or
inclined surfaces with their needle-sharp hooked claws. The most
familiar representative of the family APODIDAE (True Swifts) is our
House Swift (*Apus affinis*)—PLATE 53 (bottom)—Hindi: *Băbilā* or
Bătāsi. It is somewhat smaller than a sparrow, smoky black with
white throat, white rump, short square tail and long, narrow pointed
wings. The bird keeps in the neighbourhood of ancient forts, ruined
mosques and buildings, as well as occupied dwelling houses. Parties
are seen flying about gregariously all day long, hawking tiny winged
insects and uttering their merry twittering screams. The long stream-
lined wings enable swifts to fly almost incessantly at great speed.
Large disorderly rabbles may commonly be seen in the evenings
wheeling around, or 'balling', high up in the air uttering their
shrill, joyous twittering cries, and quite obviously enjoying
themselves. The birds build in clustered colonies plastering their
nests helter-skelter along the angle of the wall and ceiling in buildings,
and under arches and gateways, even in the heart of congested
bazars. The nests are round untidy cups made entirely of straw,
feathers, etc. cemented together with the birds' saliva. The entrance
hole may be merely a slit between the wall and the nest. The
eggs—2 to 4—are pure white elongated ovals. The same colonies or
'villages' are occupied year after year if left unmolested, the sites
becoming traditional.

The Order CORACIIFORMES is represented by the families
ALCEDINIDAE (Kingfishers), MEROPIDAE (Bee-eaters), CORACIIDAE
(Rollers), and BUCEROTIDAE (Hornbills).

The **Small Blue Kingfisher** (*Alcedo atthis*)—PLATE 54—Hindi:
Chhotā kilkilā or *Shăreefăn* is slightly larger than a sparrow. It is a
dapper little blue and green kingfisher with deep rust-coloured

underparts, short stumpy tail, and long straight pointed bill. It is usually seen singly by stream, tank, or puddle perched on a low overhanging branch, or flying swiftly close over the water. Rarely it also ventures out on rocky seashores.

As it sits on a low branch over water the bird constantly bobs its head up and down, turning it this way and that, and jerking up its stub tail to the accompaniment of a subdued *click*. All the while it is intently scanning the water below for any fish or tadpole that may come up near the surface. On sighting the quarry it drops on it with a splash, bill foremost, going under but presently reappearing with it held crosswise between the mandibles, and dashes off to a nearby perch where the victim is battered to death and swallowed. Occasionally it also hovers over the water and plunges after prey in the spectacular manner which is such a speciality of the Pied Kingfisher. A sharp *chichee-chichee* is uttered as the bird dashes at top speed low over the surface from one corner of its beat to another. Besides small fish and tadpoles, it eats water beetles and their larvae and other aquatic insects. Its favourite nesting sites are earthen banks of streams, tanks, and ditches, into which are burrowed horizontal tunnels up to a metre or more in length, ending in a widened egg chamber. This is unlined but usually littered with the smelly remains of cast-up fish bones and beetle elytra. The normal clutch consists of 5 to 7 eggs—pure white roundish ovals with a high gloss.

Another, perhaps commoner and more familiar blue kingfisher is the **Whitebreasted** (*Halcyon smyrnensis*) which is less dependent for its sustenance on water than most species, since it has switched over largely to a diet of terrestrial insects. It is about the size of a myna, brilliant turquoise blue above, with deep chocolate-brown head, neck, and underparts. A conspicuous white 'shirt front', and the long, heavy, pointed red bill confirm its identity. A large white patch on the black wings shows in flight.

The **Pied Kingfisher** (*Ceryle rudis*)—PLATE 55—Hindi: *Kōryālā kilkilā* or *Kărōna* is a bird that is not easy to overlook. In size it is between a myna and a pigeon, of speckled and barred black-and-white plumage with the typical stout dagger-shaped kingfisher bill. The male is similar to the female (illustrated) but has a gorget of two, more or less complete black bands instead of a single one slightly broken in the middle. Single birds or pairs frequent rivers, jheels, village tanks, backwaters and tidal creeks perching on a favourite stake or rock, flicking up its tail and bobbing and turning its head from time to time. Its sharp, cheery notes *chīrruk, chīrruk,* uttered on the wing are unmistakable when once heard. The most characteristic thing about the Pied Kingfisher, however, is its spectacular mode of hunting. Flying over the water, its attention is unceasingly directed below for any small fish that may venture near the surface. Immediately one is sighted the bird stops dead in its flight and, with face to wind and body tilted upright as if standing on its tail, it 'hangs' in mid-air poised over the spot on rapidly beating wings, the workmanlike bill at the ready. As soon as the quarry rises to within striking depth the bird closes its wings and hurls itself like a bolt from a height of 6 or 8 metres going completely under the water. It presently reappears with the quarry held crosswise in its bill, and with a shrug to shake off the water makes for a nearby perch where the struggling victim is battered to death, manoeuvred into position, and swallowed head foremost. The food consists mainly of fish, but tadpoles, frogs, and aquatic insects are also taken. The nest is at the end of a horizontal tunnel dug into an earthbank or cutting. It is usually unlined, but freely littered with smelly cast-up fish bones. The eggs—5 or 6—are pure white glossy roundish ovals.

The **Himalayan Pied Kingfisher** (*Ceryle lugubris*), much larger and with a prominent crest, replaces this species in the Himalayas above about 800 metres.

The **Small Green Bee-eater** (*Merops orientalis*)—PLATE 56— Hindi: *Pătringā*, is a slim grass-green bird about the size of a sparrow. Its head and neck are tinged with reddish brown, and the central pair of tail feathers are prolonged into blunt pins. The slender, long, slightly curved black bill, and a conspicuous black 'necklace' on the throat are other pointers to its identity. The bird is met with in pairs or loose flocks in open country and is partial to cultivation, forest clearings, and village grazing grounds. Loose parties are usually seen perched on telegraph wires, fence posts and bushes whence the birds launch swift and graceful aerial sorties after winged insects, circling back to the perch on outspread motionless wings after each capture. Here the struggling quarry is whacked and battered before being swallowed. The notes constantly uttered on the wing are a pleasant jingling *tit, tit* or *tree-tree-tree*. Large congregations resort to favourite leafy trees to roost at sunset. Great noise and bustle prevails before the birds finally settle for the night, the entire concourse flying out in a milling rabble every now and again without apparent cause, circling round the tree with much excited trilling, and gradually resettling. They sleep huddled together in little groups along the branches, plumage fluffed out and head tucked under the wing, and are late risers as birds go, seldom being on the move till the sun is well up. Their food consists of dragonflies and other winged insects, and bee-eaters sometimes do damage to apiary bees. The birds often nest in colonies excavating horizontal tunnels up to a metre or more long in sandy soil, in the sides of earth cuttings and borrow-pits—sometimes obliquely in sloping ground. The tunnel ends in an expanded unlined egg chamber. The eggs—5 to 7—are white roundish ovals.

A near relation, the **Bluetailed Bee-eater** (*Merops philippinus*), distinguished by its larger size, a black stripe through the eye, chestnut throat and blue tail, is also common in open country, and found chiefly at tanks and jheels. It moves about a good deal seasonally but its local migrations are as yet not properly understood.

The family CORACIIDAE is represented by the familiar **Indian Roller** or **Blue Jay** (*Coracias benghalensis*)—PLATE 57—Hindi: *Nīlkănth* or *Săbzăk*. This is a striking Oxford-and-Cambridge blue bird about the size of a pigeon, with a biggish head, heavy bill, rufous-brown breast, and pale blue abdomen and under the tail. The dark and pale blue colours in the wings show up as brilliant bands in flight. The Roller is essentially an inhabitant of open cultivated country and avoids dense forest. It is usually seen perched on an exposed tree stump or telegraph wires whence the surroundings can be surveyed to best advantage. From such look-out posts it swoops down to the ground now and again to pick up an insect, returning with the morsel to the same perch or flying leisurely across to another nearby where the victim is battered and swallowed. Crickets, grass-hoppers, beetles and other insects comprise its food almost exclusively, and the birds do great service to agriculture by the destruction of these injurious pests. Occasionally lizards, mice, and frogs are also eaten. The Roller has a variety of loud raucous calls and is parti-cularly noisy and demonstrative during its aerial courtship displays. The male then indulges in a series of fantastic aerobatics, rocketting into the air, somersaulting, nose-diving, and rolling from side to side to the accompaniment of harsh grating screams, with his brilliant plumage flashing in the sun. The nest is a collection of straw, feathers, and rubbish in a natural tree hollow. The eggs—4 or 5—are glossy, pure white roundish ovals.

An allied species, the **Kashmir Roller** (*Coracias garrulus*) which replaces the peninsular bird in Kashmir, is a common Africa-bound passage migrant over Sind, Kutch, Saurashtra and northern Gujarat in September-October. It is easily distinguished on the wing by its uniformly blue-black flight feathers (see inset on plate). Its entire underside, including the breast, is pale blue.

Our sole representative of the family UPUPIDAE is the **Hoopoe** (*Upupa epops*)—PLATE 58—Hindi: *Hūdhūd*, an arresting fawn-coloured bird with black and white zebra markings on its back, wings, and tail. A round and full fan-shaped retractable crest, and long slender slightly curved bill are additional pointers. Its size is about that of a myna. The Hoopoe is usually met with in pairs or small parties. It is fond of lawns, gardens, groves, and lightly wooded open country often in the neighbourhood of towns and villages. The birds walk or run about on ground on their squat legs with a some-what waddling quail-like gait, busily probing into the soil and amongst the fallen leaves with bill partly open like forceps. While digging, the crest is retracted and projects in a point behind the head, suggestive of a miniature pickaxe. On alarm or excitement the crest is flicked open fanwise. The bird flies off in an undulating undecided sort of way to resettle at some distance, whereupon the crest is again raised. Its call is a soft and musical *hoo-po* or *hoo-po-po* repeated several times and often intermittently for over 10 minutes at a stretch. When calling, the bird lowers and bobs its head so that the bill lies almost flat against the breast. At other times the head is jerked forward at each successive call, as if barking, and the crest opened and shut from time to time. Besides the *hoo-po* calls, it has a variety of harsh caws and chuckles. Its diet consists of insects, grubs and pupae many of which are serious agricultural pests. The birds are therefore highly beneficial to man. The nest is in a hole in a wall, roof, or under the eaves of a building, or a natural tree-hollow, untidily lined with filthy rags, hair, straw and rubbish, and is notorious for the stench it emits. The eggs—5 or 6—are white, but usually become much soiled and discoloured during incubation.

Our last family of this Order is BUCEROTIDAE, the Hornbills. They are large frugivorous and arboreal birds characterized by their outsized bills. The **Malabar Pied Hornbill** (*Anthracoceros coronatus*)—PLATE 59—Hindi: *Dhăn chiri* is a typical example. It is rather larger than the Pariah Kite, chiefly black and white. The outer feathers of the longish and broad black tail are *wholly white*. The ponderous yellow-and-black horn-shaped bill, surmounted by a pointed *flat-sided* casque is its most striking feature. This distinguishes it from the very similar **Large Pied Hornbill** (*A. malabaricus*) which has the outer tail feathers *black*, only tipped with white. Moreover, the sides of its casque are convex and not flat. The latter has a more northerly range, being found from Kumaon to Assam. The female of the Malabar species differs from the male (illustrated) in having the naked skin round the eye whitish.

All hornbills have more or less similar habits. They commonly live in wooded country with scattered trees of banyan, peepal and other species of wild fig—these fruits forming their staple food. They also eat lizards, and baby birds and rodents on occasion. The birds keep in parties which fly from tree to tree in follow-my-leader fashion in their characteristic noisy undulating style—a few rapid wing strokes followed by a dipping glide with the primaries upcurved. They all have a large variety of loud raucous roars, screams, and squeals. Their nesting habits are unique. A natural tree hollow is walled up with the bird's droppings as plaster and its bill as trowel, imprisoning the female and leaving only a narrow slit through which the male feeds her throughout the incubation period of the eggs. The wall is broken down and the female released only after the young hatch out, both parents then exerting themselves jointly to forage for them. The Pied Hornbill, like most members of the family, nests chiefly between March and June before the monsoon has set in. The eggs—2 to 4—are white when freshly laid, but become sullied during incubation.

The Order PICIFORMES includes the families CAPITONIDAE (Barbets) and PICIDAE (Woodpeckers). Barbets are mostly bright coloured but rather dumpy and inelegant arboreal fruit-eating birds with large heavy bills overhung round the base by well-developed stiff bristles. The family is exemplified by the familiar **Coppersmith** or **Crimsonbreasted Barbet** (*Megalaima haemace-phala*)—PLATE 60—Hindi: *Chhōta băsăntha*, slightly larger and more dumpy than a sparrow.

It is a heavy-billed grass-green bird with crimson breast and forehead, yellow throat, and green-streaked yellowish underparts. The short truncated tail looks distinctly triangular in flight-silhouette. The Coppersmith is equally at home in outlying forest or in the heart of a noisy city provided there are large fruiting trees of banyan, peepal and other wild figs to furnish its staple food. On such trees coppersmiths sometimes collect in large numbers to feast in company with mynas, bulbuls, green pigeons, hornbills and other frugivorous birds. Moths and winged termites are occasionally captured by ungainly and ludicrous aerial sorties from a branch. They are entirely arboreal birds and never descend to the ground. The loud monotonous calls *tūk...tūk...tūk* and so on, repeated every two seconds or so, monotonously and incessantly throughout the day, have been aptly likened to a distant coppersmith hammering on his metal. They are amongst the most familiar bird voices of the countryside. While uttering them the bird bobs its head from side to side producing a curious ventriloquistic effect. Coppersmiths lay their eggs in holes excavated by the birds themselves in decaying softwood branches, such as of the coral or drumstick trees, at moderate heights from the ground. No lining is provided. The normal clutch consists of 3 eggs, glossless white, without any markings.

Another widely distributed barbet, oftener heard than seen in forests owing to its concealing green coloration is the **Large Green Barbet** (*M. zeylanica*). It is about as large as a myna, chiefly grass-green with brownish head and neck, and a patch of naked orange skin round the eyes. Its loud familiar calls, *kutroo*, *kutroo* and so on, resound endlessly in the forest.

The woodpeckers are particularly well represented in the Indian subcontinent. This group is of great importance to forestry since the birds live largely on grubs of wood-boring beetles and other insects injurious to trees. They are extracted from the borings and pupal galleries within the trunks and branches of trees by means of the specially adapted chisel-shaped bill and worm-like extensile barb-tipped tongue, capable of being shot out far beyond the bill. One of our commonest woodpeckers is the **Mahratta Woodpecker** (*Dendrocopos mahrattensis*)—PLATE 61—Hindi: *Kātphōra* (all woodpeckers). This is a small woodpecker about the size of a bulbul with longish, stout, pointed bill and stiff wedge-shaped tail. The upper plumage is irregularly spotted black-and-white, with a brownish yellow forecrown and scarlet crest. The underparts are whitish, streaked with brown on the breast and flanks and with a scarlet-crimson patch on the abdomen and under the tail. The female lacks the scarlet on the crown. The Mahratta Woodpecker frequents light deciduous jungle, mango orchards, and even semi-desert country with sparse scrub and stunted trees. The birds usually go about in pairs flying from tree-trunk to tree-trunk, alighting low down and scuttling upward in jerky spurts, directly or in spirals, halting at intervals to tap on the bark or peer inquisitively into crevices for lurking insects. The stiff pointed tail is pressed against the stem to serve as a supporting tripod. Their diet consists of grubs and ants secured by means of their barb-pointed extensile tongue. The call notes commonly uttered are a sharp *click, click,* or *click-r-r-r.* The flight, as of all woodpeckers, is swift and undulating, attained by a series of rapid wing beats followed by short pauses. They nest in holes chiselled out by themselves in rotten branches at moderate heights. When the branch is horizontal the entrance hole is placed on the under surface to keep out the rain. The nest-hole is usually unlined. The full clutch consists of 3 eggs—glossy white and roundish.

Perhaps an equally common species in the Peninsula is the **Goldenbacked Woodpecker** (*Dinopium benghalense*) which is larger than the Mahratta—distinctive golden yellow and black above, buffy white below streaked with black. The entire crown and occipital crest is crimson in the male, only partly so in the female. This woodpecker is also found in village groves and gardens, and in lightly wooded country.

Nearly one-third of the total number of bird species found in India belong to the last Order PASSERIFORMES, popularly known as Perching Birds or Song Birds. It embraces a large number of superficially divergent families, but all characterized by the possession of certain well defined anatomical features such as the structure of the tendons of the leg and foot, of the skull and palate, and the muscles of the syrinx, *i.e.* the lower end of the windpipe or trachea which is the organ of voice production in birds. Only a few prominent Families of this Order and their more familiar representatives are dealt with here.

Family PITTIDAE—Pittas, or the so-called Ant Thrushes, are brightly coloured ground-haunting birds that live on the forest floor and dig with their stout bills amongst the damp earth and mulch for insects and grubs that comprise their food. They have strong longish legs on which they hop along like thrushes, flying seldom and only for short distances when disturbed. Some species, however, undertake long migrations.

The **Indian Pitta** (*Pitta brachyura*)—PLATE 62—Hindi: *Naorăng*, is a gaudy coloured stub-tailed myna-sized bird—green, blue, fulvous, black, and white, with crimson abdomen and under the tail. A round white spot near the tip of its wings flashes conspicuously in flight. It is fond of nullahs and ravines in scrub jungle with plenty of undergrowth, and may be met with both near and away from human habitations. Though mainly terrestrial, it roosts at night in trees. It moves on the ground in long hops like a thrush, turning over or flicking aside dead leaves and digging with its bill for food. The stumpy tail is constantly wagged, slowly and deliberately, up and down. When disturbed the bird flies up into a low branch, descending again to resume feeding as soon as the disturbance is past. Its commonest call is a loud, clear, double whistle *wheet-tew* uttered chiefly in the early morning and at dusk, but also at other times in cloudy overcast weather. This is given from the ground as well as from a branch at the rate of about 3 or 4 calls in 10 seconds, and the calling is sometimes kept up for over five minutes at a stretch. The calling bird pulls itself upright and jerks its head well back as in swallowing water. Three or four birds often reply to one another from different directions. The nest of the Pitta is a large globular structure composed of fine twigs, grass, roots, dry leaves, etc. with a circular entrance hole at the side. It is built in the fork of a low tree; sometimes on the ground under a bush. The eggs—4 to 6—are glossy china white with spots, specks, and hair-lines of dull purple.

Family ALAUDIDAE: Larks are small terrestrial, often social, birds of cryptically patterned plumage of brown, grey, sandy, black, and white. Some species are crested. They inhabit bare open country and pastureland. Some forms are migratory, others resident. Many have very beautiful songs delivered mostly from the air while soaring or hovering.

PLATE 49

CROW-PHEASANT or COUCAL
(Centropus sinensis)
(see page 67)

PLATE 50
SPOTTED OWLET
(*Athene brama*)
(*see* page 68)

PLATE 51

GREAT HORNED OWL
(*Bubo bubo*)
(*see* page 69)

PLATE 52
INDIAN NIGHTJAR
(*Caprimulgus asiaticus*)
(*see* page 70)

PLATE 53
HOUSE SWIFT (bottom)
(*Apus affinis*)
(*see* page 71)

PLATE 54
SMALL BLUE KINGFISHER
(*Alcedo atthis*)
(*see* page 71)

PLATE 55
PIED KINGFISHER
(*Ceryle rudis*)
(*see* page 72)

PLATE 56
SMALL GREEN BEE-EATER
(*Merops orientalis*)
(*see* page 73)

PLATE 57
INDIAN ROLLER or BLUE JAY
(*Coracias benghalensis*)
(*see* page 74)

PLATE 58
HOOPOE
(*Upupa epops*)
(*see* page 75)

PLATE 59

MALABAR PIED HORNBILL
(Anthracoceros coronatus)
(*see* page 76)

PLATE 60
COPPERSMITH or CRIMSONBREASTED BARBET
(*Megalaima haemacephala*)
(*see* page 77)

PLATE 61
MAHRATTA WOODPECKER
(*Dendrocopos mahrattensis*)
(*see* page 78)

PLATE 62
INDIAN PITTA
(*Pitta brachyura*)
(*see* page 80)

PLATE 63
CRESTED LARK
(*Galerida cristata*)
(*see* page 81)

PLATE 64
ASHYCROWNED or BLACKBELLIED FINCH-LARK
(*Eremopterix grisea*)
(*see* page 81)

The **Crested Lark** (*Galerida cristata*)—PLATE 63—Hindi: *Chăndūl* is slightly larger than a sparrow and distinguished by a prominent upstanding pointed crest. It is greyish earthy brown above, streaked with blackish; pale sandy below, streaked with brown on the breast. The birds are usually seen in separated pairs or family parties of 4 or 5 running about on the ground in open semi-desert country in search of food—grass and weed seeds, and small beetles and other insects. From time to time a bird mounts a clod or stone to utter its liquid whistling notes. The normal call is a pleasant *tee-ūr*. During the breeding season the male indulges in a modest song flight, soaring a few feet up in the air, flying about aimlessly over a restricted area on leisurely fluttering wings, singing its short pleasant ditty and then sailing down on stiffly outspread and slightly quivering wings to alight on a stone or clod. The song is shorter and much inferior to the lively and sustained melody of the skylark. In spite of this the *Chăndūl* is a popular cage bird and thrives well in captivity. The nest is a shallow cup of grasses lined with finer material and hair. It is placed in some slight hollow in the ground in open country under shelter of a grass-tuft or clod. The normal clutch consists of 3 or 4 eggs, dull yellowish white in colour, blotched with brown and purple.

Two smaller and more rufous-coloured crested larks between them occupy most of peninsular India, namely, **Sykes's Crested Lark** (*Galerida deva*), with few and narrow streaks on the breast, and the **Malabar Crested Lark** (*G. malabarica*), with the pectoral streaks broader and more numerous.

The **Ashycrowned** or **Blackbellied Finch-Lark** (*Eremopterix grisea*)—PLATE 64—Hindi: *Diyora, Duri,* or *Jothauli,* is a squat finch-like bird smaller than a sparrow. The male is sandy brown above, black below. It has an ashy crown and prominent whitish cheeks. The female is sandy brown all over. It is usually seen in widely scattered pairs or small flocks on the ground in dry open plains country with cultivation and waste land. Its coloration is remarkably obliterative and matches the soil to perfection. The birds shuffle along the ground in short zigzag spurts turning this way and that as they search for the grass-seeds, grain, and insects which constitute their diet. The flight

6

is a series of rapid wing beats, as in hovering, punctuated by short pauses. The male has a very pleasing little song—a combination of sweet warbling and drawn-out 'wheeching' notes—uttered from the ground as well as while performing his highly spectacular aerial display. The bird shoots vertically upward on quivering wings for 30 metres or so, and then nose-dives steeply some distance with wings pulled in at the sides. Using the momentum he suddenly turns about to face the sky and, with a few rapid flaps and wings again closed, he shoots up a few feet once more. At the crest of the wave he reverses sharply and repeats the nose-dive, and so on in descending steps till when breath-takingly near to dashing himself on the ground he flattens out and lithely comes to rest on a clod or stone. Each dive is accompanied by his pleasant little 'wheeching' song. The whole performance is soon repeated. The grace and verve with which these extravagant aerobatics are executed make them doubly fascinating to watch. The nest of this little lark is a tiny, neatly made saucer-like depression in the ground under shelter of a clod or diminutive bush in open country. It is lined with fine grasses, hair, and feathers, and frequently parapetted with gravel. The eggs—2 or 3—are pale yellowish or greyish white, blotched and speckled with brown and lavender.

The family HIRUNDINIDAE contains the Swallows and Martins. They are gregarious birds, superficially like swifts, which spend much of their time on the wing hawking tiny flying insects with the aid of their widened gapes. Their wings are long and pointed, but broader and less bow-like than in swifts. In many species the tail is deeply forked. Their flight is agile and graceful. Some species breed within our limits, others are migratory from the Palaearctic Region. One of our most familiar resident species is the **Redrumped Swallow** (*Hirundo daurica*)—PLATE 65—Hindi: *Măsjid ăbābeel*. It is about the size of a sparrow, deeply fork-tailed, glossy deep blue-black above, fulvous-white below, finely streaked with dark brown. A chestnut half collar on the hindneck, and the chestnut rump (conspicuous when banking in flight), are good recognition marks. In addition to our resident race (as above) very large numbers of a migrant form of this swallow spend the winter within our limits, usually seen perched side by side in their thousands along great stretches of telegraph wires. This migratory race is distinguished by the streaks on the underside being conspicuously broader, and by its much paler red rump.

Swallows spend a considerable part of the day hawking tiny midges and other winged insects either high up in the air or by darting sweeps close to the ground. They are social birds except in the breeding season and large congregations may be commonly seen hunting together, often in company with swifts and martins. They roost at night in enormous swarms in reedbeds and sugarcane fields, preferably those standing in water. Their flight—a few rapid wing strokes followed by a glide—is swift and graceful, the deeply forked tail adding greatly to their agility in turning and twisting to capture aerial prey. They have a cheerful twittering song in the breeding season. The nest of the Redrumped Swallow is a retort-shaped structure of plastered mud with a narrow tubular entrance, stuck flat against the ceiling of a rock-cave or dwelling house, or under a roadside culvert. The bulbous egg-chamber is lined with feathers. The eggs—3 or 4—are pure white. Another swallow commonly seen in winter in association with the Redrumped is the migratory European or so-called **Common Swallow** (*H. rustica*). It is glossy steel- or purplish blue above, pale pinkish white below. Its forehead and throat are chestnut, the latter bordered by a broad glossy black pectoral band. It also has a deeply forked tail.

Shrikes or Butcher Birds (family LANIIDAE) are mostly birds of a size between a bulbul and a myna, with large heads, stout strongly hooked bills and sharp claws—altogether like miniature hawks. The tail is graduated and the sexes similar. They are known as Butcher Birds on account of their habit, common to many of the species, of killing more than they can eat and maintaining regular larders where surplus food is impaled on thorns to be eaten at leisure. One of our common shrikes, and the largest, is the **Grey Shrike** (*Lanius excubitor*)—PLATE 66—Hindi: *Sāfēd latōra*, which is about the size of a myna. It is a striking silvery grey bird with a longish black-and-white tail. A broad black stripe runs backward from its bill through the eye. The black wings are relieved by a white patch or 'mirror' which flashes into prominence when the bird flies. The large head and heavy hooked bill give it a fierce hawk-like appearance. The bird usually keeps singly in dry open country. From an exposed perch on some thorn bush it maintains a sharp lookout for prey, pouncing to the ground from time to time to seize and carry off its victims. They are held under foot and torn to pieces with the sharp hooked bill before being swallowed. Each individual has a recognized beat or feeding territory which it will frequent day after day and jealously guard against interlopers. Its food consists of locusts, crickets and other large insects as well as lizards, mice, and young or sickly birds, sometimes much larger than itself. Its normal call notes are harsh and grating, but in the nesting season a very pleasing little tinkling song is delivered, into which are interwoven the calls of a great many other species of birds, the shrike being an excellent and convincing mimic. The nest is a deep compact cup of thorny twigs lined with rags, wool, and feathers, etc., placed in a thorny shrub at moderate height. The eggs—3 to 6—vary considerably, the commonest type being pale greenish white, thickly blotched and spotted with purplish brown.

Several other shrikes occur within our limits, one of the commonest being the **Rufousbacked** (*L. schach*). It is somewhat smaller than the Grey Shrike and has the lower back and rump bright rufous, while the underparts are washed with the same. It prefers less arid, better wooded and watered country.

Our most familiar representative of the family ORIOLIDAE (Orioles) is the **Blackheaded Oriole** (*Oriolus xanthornus*)— PLATE 67—Hindi: *Peelăk*. It is about the size of a myna, a brilliant golden-yellow arboreal bird with jet black head, throat, and upper breast, and black in the wings and tail. The bright pink bill and crimson eyes are its other conspicuous features. In the female the head is a duller black. Young birds have a yellow forehead, and the head is streaked with yellowish. The bird is commonly seen singly in wooded country. Although of a shy and retiring disposition it freely enters gardens with large leafy trees in and around villages and even in the heart of noisy cities, flashing through the foliage like a streak of gold with its peculiar strong dipping flight. Its usual call notes—a harsh *cheeah* or *kwaak* and a variety of rich melodious flute-like whistles *peelo* or *peelolo* are among the more familiar voices to gladden the heart of the birdwatcher in the countryside. Its food consists chiefly of fruits and berries, those of the banyan and peepal, and lantana, being amongst the commonest. Insects of various kinds are also eaten, as is the nectar of flowers like the brilliant red Coral (*Erythrina*) and Silk Cotton (*Salmalia*) in season. The nest of the Blackheaded Oriole is a beautifully woven deep cup of bast fibres with a copious plastering of cobwebs as binding medium. It is suspended like a hammock in the forking end-twigs of a leafy outhanging branch 4 to 10 metres up. The eggs—2 or 3—are pinkish white, spotted with black or reddish brown. For protection against crows and other marauders the nest is often built in the same tree as holds a nest of the audacious Black Drongo. Another member of the family which is also common and often found living side by side with this species is the **Golden Oriole** (*Oriolus oriolus*). It is of the same size and of an equally brilliant yellow, but lacks the black head and only has a prominent black streak through the eye instead. The Golden Oriole breeds abundantly in Kashmir and the sub-Himalayan tracts, but is chiefly met with as a winter visitor in the rest of the country.

The family DICRURIDAE (Drongos) contains slim arboreal birds of about bulbul to myna size mostly of glossy black plumage with long tails, either deeply forked or with the outer rectrices curled up at the tips, or prolonged into wire-like bare shafts ending in spatula-shaped 'rackets'. The best and most widely known member of the family is the **Black Drongo** (*Dicrurus adsimilis*)—PLATE 68—Hindi: *Būjăngā*, or *Kōtwāl*. It is a slim and agile glossy jet black bird about as big as a bulbul, with a long deeply forked tail. It is commonly seen on the open countryside and around cultivation, perched on fence-posts, bush-tops or telegraph wires etc. From these lookouts the bird swoops down to the ground to pounce on some unwary grasshopper. This is either dealt with on the spot or carried off to a perch to be held under foot and dismembered with the sharply hooked bill before being devoured. Drongos also capture moths, dragonflies, and winged termites in the air like a flycatcher and frequently live by unabashed piracy, chasing other birds—often larger than themselves—with speed and tenacity and bullying them into jettisoning their rightful prey. The birds often attend on grazing cattle, riding on the animals' backs and snapping up by aerial sorties the insects disturbed in their progress through the grass. Large numbers of drongos foregather at forest and grass fires to massacre the fleeing refugees. Altogether they destroy vast quantities of insect pests and are thus invaluable friends of the farmer. They have a number of harsh scolding or defiant calls, some closely resembling those of the Shikra Hawk, and the birds become particularly noisy when breeding. The nest is a flimsy-bottomed cup of fine twigs and grasses cemented together with cobwebs. It is built in the fork of an end twig in an outhanging branch of a large tree, usually standing by itself amidst cultivation and providing an unobstructed view of the surroundings. The eggs—3 to 5—are whitish with brownish red spots. The birds are very bold in defence of their nest, attacking and driving off birds as big as kites and crows intruding within the proximity of the nest-tree. On account of the protection thus provided, many mild-mannered birds like doves and orioles commonly nest in the same tree as harbours a drongo's nest.

Our two other common drongos that need mention are the **Ashy** (*D. leucophaeus*) and the **Whitebellied** (*D. caerulescens*). The former is slaty black with ruby-red eyes and met with in jungle rather than open fields. The latter is somewhat smaller, glossy indigo-grey above with a white belly, also found in deciduous wooded country preferably mixed bamboo jungle.

The family STURNIDAE (Starlings and Mynas) is typified by the **Common Myna** (*Acridotheres tristis*)—PLATE 69—Hindi: *Dēsi myna*. Its size is between a bulbul and a pigeon—length about 23 cm. It is a familiar perky well-groomed dark brown bird with black head, and bright yellow legs, bill, and a patch of bare skin round the eyes. A large white patch in the wings is conspicuous in flight. Along with the sparrow, crow, and pigeon, the Myna finds itself perfectly at home in the habitations of man, whether in outlying homestead or in the thick of a bustling city bazaar. It is sociable in disposition and completely omnivorous—two conditions which qualify it admirably for a life of commensalism with man. A pair or two will usually adopt a house or compound as their own and defend it vigorously against intrusion from others of their kind. But large numbers will collect to feed in harmony whether on earthworms on a freshly watered lawn, winged termites emerging from rain-sodden ground, or on a fig-laden banyan or peepal tree. The birds commonly attend on grazing cattle for the crickets and grasshoppers disturbed by the animals' feet, or follow the plough for the worms and grubs turned up with the soil, stalking jauntily alongside the bullocks, now side-hopping, now springing up in the air to seize the fleeing quarry. They share large communal roosts in trees with parakeets and crows. The Myna has a varied assortment of sharp calls and chatter, a familiar one being a loud scolding *rādio-rādio-rādio*. When resting in a shady spot during the mid-day heat the male frequently goes through as gamut of *keek-keek-keek*, *kok-kok-kok*, *churr-churr*, etc. with frowzled plumage and a ludicrous bobbing of the head towards his mate. The Myna's nest is a collection of paper, straw, and rubbish stuffed into a hole in a tree or in the wall or ceiling of a building, tenanted or otherwise. The eggs—4 or 5—are a beautiful glossy blue without any markings.

The rather similar but smaller **Bank Myna** (*A. ginginianus*) is very common in W. Pakistan and northern and northwestern India (Gujarat, Rajasthan, etc.) being particularly partial to railway stations. It is pale bluish grey instead of brown, with the naked skin round its eyes brick-red instead of yellow.

Another common myna, particularly in northern and eastern India is the **Pied Myna** (*Sturnus contra*)—PLATE 70—Hindi: *Ăblăk myna* or *Sirōli myna*, slightly smaller than the *Desi*. It is a trim black and white bird with naked orange skin round the eyes, and a deep orange-and-yellow bill. It is met with in parties and flocks in and around villages and cultivation. But though often entering gardens and compounds to hunt grasshoppers and dig up earthworms on an irrigated lawn, or to roost among large leafy trees, this myna is less dependent on man for its needs and does not appropriate nesting sites in buildings. It is also much more insectivorous and fruit-eating and less of an omnivore than its sophisticated cousin, the Common Myna. It keeps in flocks, often associated with other mynas, feeding at refuse dumps on the outskirts of towns and cities, or attending on grazing cattle on the moist grassy margins of village tanks. It has a number of high-pitched musical notes, some of them rather like snatches from the flight-song of the Blackbellied Finch-Lark (q.v.). The nest of the Pied Myna is very different from that of most of our other mynas, being a large untidy globular structure of twigs, leaves, grass, and rubbish. It is built in an outhanging branch of a mango, shīshăm or similar tree near a village or cultivation, and it is not unusual for 3 or 4 nests to be in the same tree. The eggs—4 or 5—are glossy blue, unmarked.

The Pied Myna must not be confused with the **Rosy Pastor** or **Rosecoloured Starling** (*Sturnus roseus*) which visits India in enormous swarms during winter. This is black and rose-pink (not white) but of similar size, and otherwise bearing a strong family resemblance. Rosy Pastors are seen in flocks in fields of ripening jowar and on the large red flowers of the Coral and Silk Cotton trees.

The family CORVIDAE (Crows) needs no introduction. There is nobody living in town or country who is unfamiliar with the appearance and iniquities of the ubiquitous **House Crow** (*Corvus splendens*)—PLATE 71—Hindi: *Kowwā* or *Dēsi kowwā*. Its grey neck and slightly smaller size distinguish it from its country cousin the all-black Jungle Crow. The House Crow must certainly rank as the commonest and most familiar of Indian birds. It is essentially a town-dweller, an unfailing commensal of man and almost an element of his social system. Its intelligence and audacity coupled with an uncanny instinct for scenting and avoiding danger carry it triumphantly through a life of sin and wrong-doing. Nothing comes amiss to the crow in the matter of food: a dead rat, kitchen refuse, fish pilfered from the protesting fishwife's basket, the egg or toast from your breakfast table snatched almost under your nose, are all equally welcome. But its thieving propensities are in some measure mitigated by its services as an efficient municipal scavenger. However, its ceaseless harrying of gentler ornamental and singing birds makes it thoroughly unwelcome in gardens, and the bird becomes a menace at heronries. Rabbles of crows which habitually hang around such places descend upon nests left by the owners upon disturbance from human visitors, dig into and carry off the eggs or dismember the helpless hatchlings with the utmost callousness. Although they destroy locusts and other injurious insects when they are swarming, crows also raid ripening crops such as wheat and maize and do considerable damage to fruit in orchards. Their economic status is therefore a very dubious one. The House Crow builds an untidy platform nest of sticks with a central depression lined with coir, fibre, tow, etc. It is placed up in the branches of trees normally between 3 to 8 metres up. The eggs—4 or 5— are pale blue green, speckled and streaked with brown. They closely resemble the eggs of the Koel which commonly parasitizes crows' nests. The **Jungle Crow** (*C. macrorhynchos*) is larger, uniformly glossy jet black with a heavier bill and a deeper, hoarser 'caw'. Its normal habitat is the countryside, away from towns and cities, but it often keeps on the outskirts of human habitations—about farmsteads and outlying villages, profiting from the insanitary conditions created by man.

A rather more elegant relation of the crow is the **Tree Pie** (*Dendrocitta vagabunda*)—PLATE 72—Hindi: *Măhālāt*. This is about the size of a myna but has a tail nearly 30 cm. long. It is a chestnut-brown bird with sooty head and neck. The broad black tips of its longest tail feathers and the greyish wing-coverts are particularly conspicuous in flight. The Tree Pie is found in lightly wooded country and open forest. It is of a social disposition and goes about in family parties which keep up a loud, harsh and grating conversation *ke-ke-ke-ke-ke* etc. The birds follow one another from tree to tree in follow-my-leader fashion in swift undulating flight—a

quick noisy flapping followed by a short glide on outspread wings
and tail. In addition to harsh guttural notes the birds have a wide
repertoire of quite melodious calls—one of the commonly heard
ones being a frequently repeated *Bob-o-link* or *Kokilā*. This is uttered
with the back arched, head ducked, and tail depressed in a comical
manner and is obviously directed by the male at his mate in the
breeding season. Tree Pies keep in the mixed gatherings of frugivorous
birds on banyan and peepal trees to gorge themselves on the ripe
figs. Like their cousins, the crows, they are omnivorous and will
sometimes even stoop to carrion. Normally, besides fruits and berries,
their staple diet is insects, caterpillars, lizards, nestling birds and
baby rats and mice. They hunt systematically for birds' nests, and
are highly destructive to the eggs and young of the smaller species.

The nest is a thorny twig structure like a crow's but deeper.
It is lined with finer twigs and rootlets and hidden near the top in
some densely foliaged tree. The eggs—4 or 5—are variable in coloration and markings, the commonest type being pale salmon-white
splashed and streaked with bright reddish brown.

The family CAMPEPHAGIDAE includes the Cuckoo-Shrikes and
Minivets—slim, small to medium-sized arboreal birds, usually
gregarious, chiefly insectivorous. The Minivets are a brightly
coloured group typified by the **Scarlet Minivet** (*Pericrocotus flammeus*)
—PLATE 73—Hindi: *Păhāri būlāl chăshm*. The bird is slightly smaller
than a bulbul, the adult male being mainly glossy jet black above,
orange-red to deep scarlet below. The female and young male
are grey and olive-yellow above, yellow below, with two yellow
bars in the black wings. They are usually seen in small parties of 5
or 6 in leafy treetops. In winter the birds band themselves into
flocks of 30 or more, often adult males together and females and
young males together. They keep to the foliage canopy, flitting
restlessly amongst the leaves, hovering and fluttering in front of
the sprigs to stampede lurking insects, and following one another
from tree to tree. The brilliant scarlet plumage of the males flashing
in the sun against the backdrop of dark green leaves is an exquisite
sight. Their diet consists of spiders and insects and their larvae

picked off the leaves and buds or captured in mid-air in the manner of a flycatcher. The calls frequently uttered as the troops move about are a pleasant musical *whee-tweet* or *whiriri, whiriri,* etc. The nest of all minivets is a neat shallow cup of roots and fibres bound with cobwebs and bedecked on the outside with moss, lichens, and spiders' egg cases. It is built in the crotch or on the upper surface of a branch 3 to 15 metres from the ground. The eggs—2 to 4—are pale green, spotted and blotched with dark brown and lavender.

The smaller and slimmer **Little Minivet** (*P. cinnamomeus*) is another widely distributed minivet in the Indian Union and both Pakistans. The adult male is chiefly black, grey, and orange-crimson. The female and young male have no black on head, and the red of the underparts is largely replaced by yellow: only the red rump patch as in the adult male, is retained. The Little Minivet is oftener met with in gardens and thin dry jungle than the Scarlet which prefers better wooded country.

The family IRENIDAE covers the Fairy Bluebird which is confined to the evergreen forests of the southern Western Ghats and the Eastern Himalayas. More common and widely distributed members are the Iora and Chloropses or Leaf Birds, sometimes popularly known as Green Bulbuls. The **Common Iora** (*Aegithina tiphia*)—PLATE 74—Hindi: *Shoubeegi,* about the size of a sparrow, is a glossy jet black and canary yellow bird with 2 white wing-bars. This is the male: he is usually accompanied by his mate who is largely greenish yellow with similar whitish wing-bars. In non-breeding plumage the male resembles the female but retains his black tail. The Iora is a completely arboreal insectivorous bird of gardens, groves of trees on the outskirts of villages, and light secondary jungle. Pairs go about together, hunting for caterpillars and insects among the foliage, hopping from twig to twig and clinging sideways and upside down to search under the leaves. The birds keep in touch with each other by mellow whistles and short musical chirrups. Its Hindi name *Shoubeegi* is a good onomatopoeic rendering of one of its sweet long-drawn whistles. The cock has a charming and spectacular nuptial display. He chases the hen about, posturing before her with drooping wings, white rump-feathers fluffed out and tail slightly cocked, to the accompaniment of chirruping notes, musical whistles, and a long-drawn sibilant *chee-ee*. He springs up a metre or two in the air puffing out and flaunting his glistening white rump and parachuting back to his perch in spirals, looking like a ball of fluff. The Iora's nest is a neat, compactly woven cup of soft grasses and root fibres worked into the crotch of a twig and smoothly plastered on the outside with cobwebs. The normal clutch is of 2 to 4 eggs—pale pinky white, blotched with purplish brown.

The very similar **Marshall's Iora** (*Ae. nigrolutea*) has a curiously scattered distribution in Kutch, Rajasthan, Punjab, Madhya Pradesh, and Bengal. It is distinguished chiefly by its white-tipped tail.

Muscicapidae is the most crowded family of the order Passeriformes. It is a complex of several superficially divergent subfamilies and includes the Flycatchers, Babblers, Warblers and Thrushes, united by significant anatomical and behavioural similarities, too technical for our present purpose. A few examples must suffice. A flycatcher with which many readers are probably familiar is the **Whitespotted Fantail Flycatcher** (*Rhipidura albogularis*)—PLATE 75—Hindi: *Nāchǎn* or *Chǎkdil*. This is a cheery, restless smoke-brown bird, about the size of a sparrow with conspicuous white eyebrows, white-spotted breast and flanks, and whitish abdomen. Its most striking feature is the tail, jauntily cocked and spread out like a fan, with the wings drooping on either side. The Fantail Flycatcher is at home in sparse secondary jungle as well as gardens and groves, even in the midst of noisy congested towns. It regards man with indifference and is usually charmingly tame and confiding. Pairs keep to circumscribed localities, or territories, within which they may regularly be met flitting tirelessly amongst the lower branches and from tree to tree, waltzing and pirouetting. The birds constantly launch agile and graceful looping-the-loop sallies after gnats and other tiny winged insects which are snapped up in the air with a little castanet-like click of the mandibles. The note normally uttered is a harsh *chuck-chuck*, but it also has a delightful clear whistling song of several tinkling notes, rising and falling in scale, which is constantly warbled as the bird prances about. Its food consists chiefly of mosquitoes, flies, and other dipterous insects. The nest is a beautiful little cup, like a wine glass, built of fine grasses and fibres and neatly draped and plastered on the outside with cobwebs. It is similar to the Iora's nest but differs consistently in having an untidy wisp of strips of bark etc. dangling below—not neatly rounded off as in the Iora's nest. It is built in the crotch or fork of end twigs in a low tree like a mango or chikoo graft, seldom more than about 3 metres up.

The normal clutch is of 3 eggs, pinkish cream-coloured, with a ring of minute brown specks round the broad end.

The closely related **Whitebrowed Fantail Flycatcher** (*R. aureola*), distinguished by its broad white forehead and white underparts, is common more or less throughout the Indian subcontinent.

Always exciting to see is the exquisite and fairy-like **Paradise Flycatcher** (*Terpsiphone paradisi*)—PLATE 76—Hindi: *Shāh būlbūl* or *Doodhrāj*. It is about the size of a bulbul excluding the tail ribbons which are between some 25 and 30 cm. long. The adult male is silvery white with two long ribbon-like feathers, or 'streamers', in his tail and glossy metallic black, crested head. The female and young male are chestnut above, greyish white below, also with black crested head. The young male has chestnut streamers in his tail; the female is without them and is altogether very like a bulbul in general effect. This delightful flycatcher, variously known as Rocket Bird, Widow Bird, and Ribbon Bird, is a frequenter of shady groves and gardens and thin deciduous jungle with bamboo-clad nullahs. Pairs usually keep by themselves or in association with hunting parties of other small insectivorous birds. The lithe, ethereal movements of the male as he makes his agile twisting and looping sorties after winged insects, his streamers cutting whiplash figures in the air, or as he flies in graceful undulations from one glade to another, present a spectacle of unforgettable charm. However, contrary to expectation from such loveliness, the bird possesses no song. Its only calls are a lively but harsh and grating *chē* or *chē-chwē* supplemented during the breeding season by a number of pleasant musical notes uttered by both sexes—the nearest approach to song. The food, typical of the flycatchers, consists of flies, gnats, and moths, etc. captured mostly on the wing. The Paradise Flycatcher nests in many parts of the subcontinent, but it is one of the commonest breeding birds in the Vale of Kashmir and adds immeasurably to the fascination of the country for the nature-loving visitor. The nest is a compactly woven cup of fine grasses and fibres plastered on the exterior with cobwebs and spiders' egg cases. It is built in the crotch or elbow of a twig, normally between 2 and 5 metres from the ground. The eggs—3 to 5—are pale creamy pink with specks and blotches of reddish brown.

The Babblers are a large and heterogeneous assemblage of small to medium sized birds of plain brown to brightly coloured plumage and chiefly gregarious habit. The following are some of the commoner and better known representatives of this subfamily (Timaliinae).

The **Yellow-eyed Babbler** (*Chrysomma sinensis*)—PLATE 77— Hindi: *Būlāl chăshm*, slightly smaller than a bulbul, is a longish-tailed bird of grass-and-scrub jungle and shrubbery. It is cinnamon and chestnut-brown above, white below, with conspicuous orange-yellow eyelids and yellow eyes. Like most of the family it is normally met with in small parties of 5 to 7 birds frequenting thorn scrub and tall grass jungle, or coarse grass tussocks growing on bunds separating cultivated fields. The birds hunt among the brushwood for insects, clambering up the grass stems and often clinging to them sideways or upside down in the manner of tits. They are great skulkers, and when alarmed will hop quickly from bush to bush and vanish through the undergrowth emitting harsh tittering notes of concern. The calls normally uttered are a clear, loud, and somewhat plaintive *cheep-cheep-cheep*. In the breeding season the males clamber up to exposed situations on bushtop or grass blade and deliver a loud and pretty cheeping song. Their food consists of spiders, grasshoppers and other insects, but like most of their relations the birds are very fond of flower nectar, and regular visitors to the showy blossoms of the Coral and Silk Cotton trees whenever available. The nest of the Yellow-eyed Babbler is a deep cup of coarse grasses lined with finer material and copiously plastered on the outside with cobwebs. It

is wedged into the crotch of a bush, or slung hammock-wise between
the upright stems of grasses or monsoon plants usually under
2 metres from the ground. The eggs—4 or 5—are yellowish white
in colour, finely speckled with purplish brown.

The **Jungle Babbler** (*Turdoides striatus*)—PLATE 78—Hindi:
Sāt bhāi or *Ghonghāi*, is an earthy brown, frowzled and untidy-looking
bird slightly smaller than a myna, with a longish tail that gives the
impression of being loosely stuck into the body. It is invariably seen
in flocks of half a dozen or so whence the Hindi name, and also
'Seven Sisters' in English. The Jungle Babbler inhabits outlying
jungle as well as well wooded gardens, compounds, and groves of
trees in and around towns and villages. The 'sisterhoods' spend their
time hopping on the ground rummaging among the fallen leaves for
insects. They habitually form the nucleus of the mixed itinerant
hunting parties of insectivorous birds that move about in the forest.
The birds keep up a constant harsh conversational chatter and
squeaking, and as a rule the best of good fellowship prevails within
the sisterhood. But occasionally differences of opinion arise between
the members, and loud discordant wrangling ensues when bill and
claws are freely plied and feathers fly. Such lapses, however, are few
and far between and short-lived, and normal cordiality is soon
restored. To outside threat or aggression the sisterhood presents a
solid front; when one member of the flock happens to be set upon
by a cat or hawk, the others promptly rally to his rescue attacking
the marauder with boldness and determination and much loud
swearing, usually putting it to flight. Their food consists of spiders,
cockroaches, moths, and other insects and larvae. Banyan and peepal
figs, lantana and other berries, as well as seeds and grain are also
eaten. Babblers are inordinately fond of the nectar of Silk Cotton
and Coral flowers and contribute significantly towards their cross-
pollination in their efforts to reach the liquid. The nest is a loosely
built cup of twigs and rootlets in the fork of a leafy branch, 3 to 5
metres above the ground. The clutch consists of 3 or 4 eggs of a
beautiful turquoise blue. Cooperative building, and feeding of nest-
young by several members of a sisterhood besides the actual parents
has been frequently observed, and may even be the normal practice.

Jungle Babbler nests are commonly parasitized by the Pied Crested and Hawk-Cuckoos both of which lay similar blue eggs.

Another familiar member of the babbler group is the **Common Babbler** (*Turdoides caudatus*)—PLATE 79—Hindi: *Dumri* or *Chichil*, about as big as a bulbul with a relatively longer tail. It is slimmer than the Jungle Babbler, but like it invariably seen in flocks or 'sisterhoods' of half a dozen or so on the ground and among low thorn bushes. Its earthy brown upper plumage is streaked darker, and the long graduated loosely attached tail is finely cross-rayed. The sisterhoods spend their time scuttling along the ground like rats, running fast with short mincing steps under hedges and through thorny scrub and thickets, rummaging for insects and caterpillars. They are loth to take wing and usually rely on their nimble legs for escape when alarmed or while moving from bush to bush. Their flight is feeble—a few rapid flaps of the rounded wings followed by a glide on outspread wings and tail. Their call is a series of short pleasant trilling whistles. When agitated, as on sighting a snake or cat, the birds utter a musical whistling *which-which-whichi-ri-ri-ri-ri-ri-ri* etc. as they nervously twitch their wings and tail and hop from bush to bush peering down at the intruder, the entire sisterhood combining to hurl a disorderly chorus of loud invectives at him. The food consists of spiders, insects, berries, seeds, and grain and flower-nectar. The nest is a neat, compact cup of grass and rootlets placed in a low thorn bush seldom more than about 2 metres up. The eggs—3 or 4 —are glossy turquoise blue, and as with the Jungle and Large Grey Babblers, their nests are commonly parasitized by the Pied Crested and Hawk-Cuckoos whose eggs match theirs in coloration.

A closely allied species, the **Large Grey Babbler** (*T. malcolmi*), greyer brown with grey forehead and white outer tail feathers (conspicuous when tail spread in flight) is also common in the drier parts of the Peninsula generally, and plentiful on the Deccan plateau.

The Warblers are mostly tiny birds of sober coloration, smaller than sparrows, whose characteristics as a group are difficult to describe. Many species are resident and others migratory. The

PLATE 65
REDRUMPED SWALLOW
(*Hirundo daurica*)
(*see* page 82)

0   5 CM   HM

PLATE 66
GREY SHRIKE
(*Lanius excubitor*)
(*see* page 83)

PLATE 67
BLACKHEADED ORIOLE
(*Oriolus xanthornus*)
(*see* page 84)

PLATE 68
BLACK DRONGO
(*Dicrurus adsimilis*)
(*see* page 85)

PLATE 69
COMMON MYNA
(*Acridotheres tristis*)
(*see* page 86)

PLATE 70
PIED MYNA
(*Sturnus contra*)
(*see* page 87)

PLATE 71
HOUSE CROW
(Corvus splendens)
(*see* page 88)

PLATE 72
TREE PIE
(*Dendrocitta vagabunda*)
(*see* page 89)

PLATE 73
SCARLET MINIVET
(*Pericrocotus flammeus*)
(*see* page 90)

PLATE 74
COMMON IORA
(*Aegithina tiphia*)
(*see* page 91)

WHITESPOTTED FANTAIL FLYCATCHER
(Rhipidura albogularis)
(*see* page 92)

PLATE 76
PARADISE FLYCATCHER
(*Terpsiphone paradisi*)
(*see* page 93)

PLATE 77
YELLOW-EYED BABBLER
(*Chrysomma sinensis*)
(*see* page 94)

PLATE 78
JUNGLE BABBLER
(*Turdoides striatus*)
(*see* page 95)

PLATE 79
COMMON BABBLER
(*Turdoides caudatus*)
(*see* page 96)

PLATE 80
ASHY WREN-WARBLER
(*Prinia socialis*)
(*see* page 97)

subfamily—Sylviinae—is exemplified by the following common and familiar representatives.

The **Ashy Wren-Warbler** (*Prinia socialis*)—PLATE 80—Hindi: *Phūtki* (for most warblers), is ashy slate-coloured above, fulvous white below, with a loose, longish, graduated black-and-white-tipped tail. It is carried partially cocked and constantly shaken up and down. The plumage becomes browner (less slaty) in winter. This little warbler is a frequent inhabitant of large well watered gardens with shrubbery and herbaceous borders. Though not shy, it is of a retiring disposition and hops about quietly among the bushes with cocked and loosely switching tail in search of insects and caterpillars, uttering a sharp *tee-tee-tee* from time to time. In the breeding season, however, the male courts publicity, constantly climbing up to some exposed branch or bushtop and delivering a torrent of spirited warbling. He flits about excitedly, jerks his tail up and down, and flutters his wings. His jerky see-saw display flight gives the impression of the tail being too heavy for him to carry. When suddenly disturbed off its nest and agitatedly flitting around, this warbler in common with the next and some of its other near relations, emits a peculiar sharp *kit-kit-kit* as of electric sparks, presumably by snapping its bill, but the source is not proven. The normal nest of the Ashy Wren-Warbler is of the Tailor Bird type—in a funnel of sewn leaves—but in situations where the requisite large pliant leaves are not available the nest is an oblong purse of woven fibres into which some supporting small leaves are tacked with cobwebs. The nest is normally under 1½ metres from the ground. The eggs—3 or 4—are a beautiful glossy brick-red with a dark ring round the broad end.

The **Indian Wren-Warbler** (*P. subflava*) is rufous earthy brown, rather like the Ashy in winter plumage. It can be distinguished by the absence of the terminal spots on the tail and by its preference for drier, less well watered localities.

Our best known warbler on merit and through well deserved publicity in Kipling's immortal *Jungle Book* is the *Dărzi* or **Tailor Bird** (*Orthotomus sutorius*)—PLATE 81—a sprightly little olive-green bird with whitish underparts, a rust coloured crown, and long narrow pin-shaped middle feathers to its jauntily cocked tail. It is

7

seen singly or in pairs in shrubbery and gardens and is equally at home in town and country. The bird is everywhere tame and confiding and will fearlessly enter verandahs of inhabited bungalows, hopping about on the floor to pick up bits of thread or wisps of cotton wool for its nest, or to hunt among the creepers on the trellis work or potted plants, within a few feet of the inmates. Its loud cheerful calls *towit-towit-towit* or *pretty-pretty-pretty* are amongst the more familiar bird voices in suburban gardens. Its food, as of other warblers, consists of tiny insects and their eggs and caterpillars, but the bird is also very partial to flower-nectar and may invariably be seen probing for this into the showy red blossoms of the Silk Cotton and Coral trees. The Tailor Bird is justly renowned for its remarkable nest which indeed reflects the high water mark of avian architectural design. The nest itself is a rough cup of soft fibres, hair, cotton wool and vegetable down, but it is placed in a funnel skilfully fashioned by folding over and stitching a broad green leaf along its edges. When the leaf is not sufficiently large two or more are thus sewn together. The stitching material is cotton or vegetable down twisted into a thread and cleverly knotted at the ends to prevent the sewing getting undone by the tension. Crotons, figs and similar large-leaved plants or creepers are selected, frequently those growing in pots in a porch or verandah and seldom more than a metre or two up. The eggs—3 or 4—are reddish- or bluish white, usually spotted with brownish red.

Thrushes, Robins, and Chats also form an important subfamily of the flycatchers (Turdinae). The **Magpie Robin** (*Copsychus saularis*)—PLATE 82—Hindi: *Dǎiyǎr* or *Dǎiya*, is a common and familiar example. The male is a trim black-and-white bird usually seen with the tail cocked; in the female the black portions are replaced by brown and slaty grey. The birds keep singly or in pairs in thin jungle, but most commonly in the neighbourhood of human habitations. In the non-breeding season the male is quiet and unobtrusive, skulking in shrubbery and undergrowth and only uttering a plaintive *swee-ee* and harsh *chr-r, chr-r* notes from time to time. But with the approach of the hot weather he regains his voice and asserts himself as one of our finest songsters. In his spruce and glistening pied livery he cuts a happy figure as from the topmost twig of a leafless tree or gate post within his territory he pours out a continuous torrent of joyous and far-reaching song, which though not so rich as the Shāma's is no less spirited. The tail is depressed and partly spread while singing, but constantly jerked upward and flicked open as if to punctuate the melody. The singing continues intermittently throughout the day and often well into the dusk. When staking out their territories, and during the breeding season, the males are very pugnacious. They show off before their mates as well as intruding rivals by a cocking of the outspread tail right over the back, chest puffed out ludicrously, bill pointing skyward while the bird stiffly struts and nods. The diet is chiefly insectivorous, but they will occasionally take berries, and nectar of the showy red flowers of the Silk Cotton and Coral trees forms an irresistible attraction at all times. The nest is a pad of grass, rootlets, and hair placed in a hole in a wall or tree-trunk, or in the top of a drain pipe or derelict street lamp. Nest boxes are freely patronized. The eggs—3 to 5—are some shade of pale blue-green, blotched and mottled with reddish brown.

A smaller relation of the Magpie Robin is the **Pied Bushchat** (*Saxicola caprata*)—PLATE 83—Hindi: *Kālā pidda*, about the size of a sparrow. The male is jet black with contrasting glistening white patches on the rump, lower abdomen, and wings—the last more prominent in flight. The female is plain earth-brown with a pale rust coloured rump. The bird is found patchily, partly as resident partly as winter visitor, and keeps in separated pairs in open broken country and around cultivation, perched on bushtops and reed stems. From here it makes frequent little darts to the ground to pick up a grasshopper or bug. Sometimes it captures winged insects by springing vertically up into the air or making short flycatcher-like sorties. The note commonly uttered is a harsh *chek, chek* ending in a subdued *trweet*. In the breeding season the male delivers a pretty little whistling song beginning with a double *chik-chik* and somewhat resembling the song of the Indian Robin. The song is given within his territory, during courtship and also as a challenge to intruding rivals, and is accompanied by various threatening postures. The nest is a pad of grass lined with hair or wool, placed in a hollow in an earth cutting or wall. The eggs—3 or 5—are pale bluish white, speckled and blotched with reddish brown.

The **Collared Bushchat** (*Saxicola torquata*) is also found in cultivation and tall grassland during the winter. The male has a black head, orange-brown breast, and prominent white patches on the sides of the neck (the 'collar'), wings and above the base of the tail. The female resembles the Pied Bushchat's but is streaked darker on the upper parts.

The **Indian Robin** (*Saxicoloides fulicata*)—PLATE 84—Hindi: *Kālchuri*, is another member of the thrush group and one of the more familiar and confiding birds of our countryside, frequently met with in villages perched on a thatch roof, roadside hedge or stone, switching its cocked tail up and down expressively as it turns facing this way and that, uttering its cheery notes. The male is a sprightly little brown and glistening black bird with deep chestnut under its permanently cocked tail. He has a white patch on his wings concealed or almost so at rest but flashing into prominence when he flies. The hen is ashy brown with paler chestnut under the likewise cocked tail. The birds spend their time running about in spurts, now mounting a bush or termite mound now descending to pick up some tiny insect prey. In this quest the birds will boldly enter verandahs of huts and bungalows regardless of the activities of the inmates. The Robin's food is exclusively insects and caterpillars, it is partial to white ants and commonly in attendance at ant hills; its song is no more than a few sprightly and cheerful notes. This is given by the male chiefly in courtship display or when confronting an interloper into his territory, when he will also puff out his chest and stretch himself menacingly to his full height, tossing the cocked tail forward well over his back. The Indian Robin's nest is a cup of grass and rootlets, frequently adorned with snake sloughs. It is placed in a hole in an earth cutting, rotten tree stump, or in a derelict tin can or earthen chatty. The eggs—2 or 3—are white with a creamy or greenish tinge, speckled and blotched with ruddy brown.

One of our most distinguished songsters in the thrush subfamily is the **Malabar Whistling Thrush** (*Myiophoneus horsfieldii*)—PLATE

85—Hindi: *Kāstūrā*. It is a handsome largish blue-black thrush, between a myna and pigeon in size, with patches of glistening cobalt blue on its forehead and shoulders, and black bill and legs. The bird is a denizen of well wooded rocky nullahs and torrential hill streams, both near and away from human habitations. Its loud and rich whistling song, heard during the breeding season, is one of the earliest bird voices to greet the dawn. The astonishingly human quality of its melody and its aimless rambling up and down the scale has earned the bird its rather apt popular names of Idle or Whistling Schoolboy. Like other thrushes it is silent during the non-breeding season, the only note then uttered being the characteristic sharp *kree-ee* of the family. The food of the Whistling Thrush consists of aquatic insects, snails and crabs. The latter are purposefully battered on stones to remove their hard covering. The bird hops from stone to stone amidst a swirling stream and snatches at the quarry as it drifts past. The tail is constantly flicked open fanwise and jerked up and down till it almost touches the perch, evidently in an attempt to stampede prey lurking in the hollows and fissures in the rocks. The Whistling Thrush is much prized by fanciers as a songster and becomes quite tame if taken as a nestling. The nest is a large compact pad of roots, moss, and grass reinforced with mud, placed under a shelving rock or on a precipitous ledge often near or under a cascading waterfall. The full clutch consists of 3 or 4 eggs, pale buff or greyish stone in colour, blotched and speckled with reddish brown and lavender.

The closely related **Himalayan Whistling Thrush** (*M. temminckii*) occupies a strip of country along the Himalayan foothills, extending into Assam and Burma. It is distinguished by a *yellow* instead of black bill, and it has no cobalt patches on the forehead or shoulders.

The family PARIDAE (Tits) contains birds mostly of the size of a sparrow or less. They are lively and vivacious arboreal birds with small stout bills, and some of them possess jaunty upstanding crests. They are richly represented in the Himalayas. Of the three species found in the Peninsula, the one that has the widest distribution is the

Grey Tit (*Parus major*)—PLATE 86—Hindi: *Rāmgangra*. It is a perky sparrow-like bird identified by its uncrested glossy black head, glistening white cheeks, grey back, and whitish underparts with a broad black band running down the middle. It is found among trees in wooded localities, but it avoids humid evergreen forest. The birds go about singly or in pairs or small parties, sometimes in association with cooperative bands of other insectivorous species. They scatter to feed among the foliage, keeping in touch with each other by joyous cheeping and twittering contact notes. They climb about, clinging to the sprigs and flowering stems upside down and in all manner of acrobatic positions, peering under leaves, probing into flowers, and searching the crevices of the bark for insects and their eggs and grubs which comprise their diet. In spite of some little damage tits may occasionally do to orchard fruit and buds, they are beneficial birds on account of the vast quantities of insect pests they destroy. They also eat the kernels of nuts and hard-shelled seeds, holding them down under foot and hacking them open by repeated hammer blows of the strong bill. In the breeding season the male delivers a clear whistling song *wheechichi, wheechichi, wheechichi*, etc. The nest of the Grey Tit is a pad of hair, moss, and feathers in a hole in a tree-trunk or branch, or in a stone wall. The eggs—4 to 6—are white or pinkish white, spotted and speckled with reddish brown.

The other common tit with a peninsular distribution is the **Yellow-cheeked** (*Parus xanthogenys*). It is a dainty black-and-yellow tit with a prominent pointed black crest and yellow underparts with a broad black band down the middle. It affects more or less the same type of country as the Grey Tit, but may also be found in damper localities.

The Nuthatches (family SITTIDAE) are small arboreal or cliff haunting birds that run along in jerky spurts up and down tree-trunks and branches or rock faces searching for spiders and insects among the fissures and crevices. They have short square tails and longish woodpecker-like bills. A species that is found practically throughout the Indian Union and in East Pakistan is the **Chestnutbellied Nuthatch** (*Sitta castanea*)—PLATE 87—Hindi:

Siri or *Kātphoriya*. It is smaller than the sparrow, slaty blue above, deep chestnut below, with longish pointed bill. The underparts of the female are paler. It is usually seen singly or in separated pairs creeping like a mouse up and around the branches and trunks of trees in light forest. The bird is partial to mango topes and groves of large trees around villages. Its feeding habits resemble both the tit and the woodpecker: like the former it scours the trunks and branches, scuttling jerkily up, sideways, or upside down, and peering inquisitively into fissures; like the woodpecker it climbs and taps away on the bark to dislodge lurking prey. In this quest the bird will often cling to and run along the undersurface of a bough with amazing agility. Its food consists of spiders, and insects with their eggs and larvae, but like the tits it also eats the kernels of various nuts and hard-shelled seeds of forest trees, wedging them firmly in some crevice and hacking them open with repeated hammer blows of the strong pointed bill. The notes it normally utters are feeble mousy squeaks, but it also has pleasant quick-repeated, double, whistling *chip-chip*. Except when paired in the breeding season the birds move about in small scattered parties, frequently in association with tits in the mixed roving bands of insectivorous birds in forest. This nuthatch lays its eggs in natural tree hollows or barbet holes, lining them with leaves, moss, and wool. The opening is walled up with a plaster of wet mud which soon dries hard leaving a small neat round hole for entrance and exit. The eggs—2 to 6—are white speckled with red.

The family MOTACILLIDAE (Pipits and Wagtails) contains slim elegant birds with longish tails which are constantly wagged up and down as they run about on grassy or marshy land picking up tiny insects. The majority of species are winter visitors to our area from the Palaearctic Region. One of the commonest of these winter visitors is the **White Wagtail** (*Motacilla alba*)—Hindi: *Dhōbăn* or *Khănjăn*, which is the size of a sparrow, but slimmer and with a longer tail. It is chiefly grey above, white below. In winter plumage the black bib (illustrated) is much reduced or wanting, the chin and throat being white like the underparts. The bird is usually seen singly or in twos and threes and small scattered parties, running about on the ground with quick mincing steps, wagging their tails incessantly as they make short lively spurts to pick up insects, turning and twisting this way and that and some-times taking short upward leaps in their pursuit. They keep to open country, ploughed fields and fallow land, and are commonly seen on golf links and maidans even in populous human habitations, hunting unconcernedly among the multitude of players of cricket and other games. The flight, typical of the family, is a series of long undulating curves caused by alternate quick flapping and closing of the wings. It is accompanied by the distinctive call *chichip, chichip, chichip*. The birds roost in vast congregations among the foliage of leafy trees, or within reedbeds and sugarcane fields. The majority of our wintering wagtails breed in northern countries beyond our limits. One race of the White Wagtail breeds in Kashmir. The nest is cup-shaped, made of grass, rootlets and wool. It is placed under a stone or bush, or among the roots of an uprooted tree near a stream or on a shingle islet in its middle. The eggs—4 to 6—are white, freckled and spotted with reddish brown.

The **Grey Wagtail** (*Motacilla caspica*)—PLATE 88 (top)—is another species widely found in winter in the better wooded parts of the subcontinent, usually seen running about singly near rocky streams and trickles, and at rain-water runnels along hill roads and forest paths. While the birds are with us the sexes are alike and without the black chin, throat and breast which the male acquires in his summer (breeding) plumage as shown in the plate. Its general habits do not differ from those of the White and other wagtails. The male has a pretty little song in the breeding season. Its nearest breeding area is in Kashmir and the western Himalayas. The nest and its site are similar to those of the White Wagtail, the eggs—4 to 6—being yellowish grey or greenish, freckled with reddish brown.

Several other grey and yellow wagtails (*M. flava*) visit us in winter. It is difficult to distinguish the various species in winter plumage, but they can be identified just before their return to their northern homelands when many of the birds have donned their distinctive summer dresses. The only resident wagtail in peninsular India is

PLATE 81
TAILOR BIRD
(*Orthotomus sutorius*)
(*see* page 97)

PLATE 82
MAGPIE ROBIN
(*Copsychus saularis*)
(*see* page 98)

PLATE 83

PIED BUSHCHAT
(Saxicola caprata)
(see page 99)

PLATE 84
INDIAN ROBIN
(*Saxicoloides fulicata*)
(*see* page 100)

MALABAR WHISTLING THRUSH
(*Myiophoneus horsfieldii*)
(*see* page 100)

PLATE 86
GREY TIT
(*Parus major*)
(*see* page 102)

PLATE 87
CHESTNUTBELLIED NUTHATCH
(*Sitta castanea*)
(*see* page 102)

5 CM

JPirani

PLATE 90
TICKELL'S FLOWERPECKER
(*Dicaeum erythrorhynchos*)
(*see* page 106)

PLATE 91
PURPLE SUNBIRD
(*Nectarinia asiatica*)
(*see* page 107)

PLATE 92
WHITE-EYE
(*Zosterops palpebrosa*)
(*see* page 108)

PLATE 93
HOUSE SPARROW
(*Passer domesticus*)
(*see* page 109)

PLATE 94
BAYA WEAVER BIRD
(*Ploceus philippinus*)
(*see* page 110)

PLATE 95
SPOTTED MUNIA (3)
(Lonchura punctulata)

PLATE 99

RED MUNIA (4)
(Estrilda amandava)
(see page 111)

JPIrani

0   5 CM

PLATE 96
COMMON INDIAN or HODGSON'S ROSEFINCH
(*Carpodacus erythrinus*)
(*see* page 112)

PLATE 97
BLACKHEADED BUNTING (top)
(*Emberiza melanocephala*)

REDHEADED BUNTING (bottom)
(*E. bruniceps*)
(*see* page 113)

the **Large Pied Wagtail** (*M. maderaspatensis*)—PLATE 88 (bottom)—
which is larger than the rest, being about the size of a bulbul. Its
plumage is black and white resembling in pattern that of the familiar
Magpie Robin, but it has a prominent white eyebrow and it does not
carry its tail cocked. This wagtail is usually met with in pairs in the
neighbourhood of jheels and village tanks and is particularly fond
of clear shingly and rocky smooth-running streams. The birds are
not shy and often frequent human habitations, perching on roof-tops
or running about and feeding unconcernedly at dhobi ghāts and the
like. They have a number of loud pleasant whistling calls, and during
the breeding season the male sings sweetly from a rock or house-top.
In a general way the ditty is not unlike some snatches of the Magpie
Robin's song. The nest is a cup-shaped pad of rootlets, hair, wool
and dry algae placed in a hole in a wall, beneath a projecting rock,
among the rafters of an inhabited dwelling, or under the girders of
a bridge. Whatever the situation, it is always near water. The
normal clutch consists of 3 or 4 eggs. They are greyish-, brownish-,
or greenish white in colour, blotched and streaked with various shades
of brown.

Pipits belong to the same family as wagtails and are similar to them
in size and shape, and largely also in habits. They are, however,
all of a sober brown coloration, like larks but with slenderer more
elongate bodies and longer tails. Some of the species are easy enough
to recognize by their size, colour pattern and habitat preferences;
others are so alike superficially that they are almost impossible to
differentiate in the field. Most of the species are winter visitors. One
of the more common and widespread of the migratory pipits is the
Tree Pipit (*Anthus trivialis*)—PLATE 89—Hindi: *Rūgēl* or *Chārchāri*
(all pipits). It is rather like the female House Sparrow in coloration
but slimmer, and with a thinner bill and longer tail. The outer tail
feathers are white and show up conspicuously when the bird is alighting from flight. Its upperparts are black-streaked sandy brown, with
a distinct pale supercilium or eyebrow. The underparts are fulvous
white heavily streaked with black on the breast. The Tree Pipit is
found in winter more or less over the entire subcontinent in

deciduous wooded country, mango orchards, and groves of trees near villages. It is distinguished from most other pipits by its habit of feeding in the shade of trees rather than in the open. Its coloration makes it completely invisible among the fallen dry leaves when it is not moving. It walks about quietly on the ground picking up weevils and other small insects which constitute its food. On disturbance it flies up into the nearby trees, descending to resume its activity as soon as the coast is clear. The notes uttered on the wing are a feeble *tseep-tseep*. The pretty song of the male, uttered during a short display flight is only heard on its northern breeding grounds beyond our borders.

Our only resident pipit is the **Indian Pipit** (*A. novaeseelandiae*). It has a very wide distribution in the subcontinent and commonly breeds in the plains. It is usually met with singly or in separated pairs in open country—on fallow land and village grazing grounds—running about briskly and slowly wagging its tail up and down. The notes, uttered on the wing, are a feeble *pipit-pipit*, etc. During the breeding season the male soars and flutters a few feet up in the air uttering a feeble cheeping song, and descends to earth again in a couple of minutes. The nest of the Indian Pipit is a shallow cup of grass, rootlets, and hair—sometimes partially domed—placed on the ground in an old hoof-print of cattle or under shelter of a clod or diminutive bush. The eggs—3 or 4— are yellowish- or greyish white irregularly blotched and spotted with brown, more densely at the broad end.

The family DICAEIDAE (Flowerpeckers) contains tiny, restless, arboreal short-tailed birds with slender, slightly curved pointed bills adapted for probing into flowers. A species with very wide distribution in the Indian Union and East Pakistan is **Tickell's Flowerpecker** (*Dicaeum erythrorhynchos*)—PLATE 90—Hindi: *Phoolchūki* (all flowerpeckers). It is an active olive-brown and greyish little bird, much smaller than a sparrow, and perhaps the smallest in India. It looks somewhat like a female sunbird but has a shorter, flesh-coloured bill. Its food consists almost exclusively of flower-nectar and berries, especially those of the injurious plant parasites of the mistletoe family (*Loranthus* and *Viscum*) commonly known in Hindi as *Bāndhā*. It fertilizes the flowers of the *Loranthus* parasite by cross-pollinating them in its efforts to reach the nectar. The ripe berries of this as well as *Viscum* are swallowed entire, the sticky, slimy seeds soon being excreted on a branch of a neighbouring tree where they adhere and germinate to spread the infestation. Flowerpeckers have regular 'beats' or feeding territories within which they make their circuits from one infested tree to another. In flight as well as while it hops restlessly among the parasite clumps the bird utters an almost incessant *chik-chik-chik*, varied occasionally by a feeble twittering song. The nest of this flowerpecker is a hanging oval pouch, somewhat smaller and neater than a sunbird's and without the drapery of rubbish on the outside. It is made of soft fibres and vegetable down, with the texture of felt, usually pinkish brown in colour and suspended from a twig some 3 to 10 metres from the ground. The eggs, normally 2, are white without any markings.

Another common flowerpecker of rather similar appearance and habits is the **Thickbilled Flowerpecker** (*D. agile*). It may be distinguished by its faintly brown-streaked underparts and the thick bluish horny finch-like bill.

The family NECTARINIIDAE—(Sunbirds or Honeysuckers) contains small brilliantly metallic coloured birds like flowerpeckers but with longer and slenderer bills specially adapted for eating nectar from flowers aided by tubular suctorial tongues. One of the commonest examples is the **Purple Sunbird** (*Nectarinia asiatica*) —PLATE 91—Hindi: *Shăkărkhŏrā* (all sunbirds), smaller than a sparrow. The male in breeding plumage is black with a high metallic sheen of green and purple, and with a tuft of fiery orange-red feathers at the 'armpits'. The non-breeding male is somewhat like the female —olive-brown above, pale dull yellow below—but with *black* wings and a broad black streak running down the middle of the breast. Sunbirds usually go about in pairs, flitting restlessly from flower to flower, clinging to them upside down and in all manner of positions to probe into the corolla with their slender curved bill for nectar, which forms their staple diet. One will sometimes hover in front of a blossom like a hawkmoth and, poised momentarily on rapidly vibrating wings, pick up a spider or small insect from it. This, however, is not its normal method of sucking nectar as in the un- related Humming Birds of the New World. It utters a short mono- syllabic *wich*, *wich* as it flits among the flower-laden branches. Breeding males love to sit in exposed situations such as a leafless treetop or telegraph wire, and sing excitedly, pivoting from side to side and nervously raising and lowering the wings to display the brilliant yellow and scarlet tuft of feathers at the 'armpits', while the tail is flicked open and shut. The song is a spirited but rather squeaky *cheewit-cheewit-cheewit*, etc. rapidly repeated. The nest— typical of the sunbirds—is a hanging oblong pouch of soft grasses, rubbish and cobwebs, draped on the outside with pieces of papery bark and caterpillar droppings. It is often built in creepers covering the wall of an inhabited bungalow, or in a low shrub, usually under 3 metres from the ground. The eggs—2 or 3—are greyish- or greenish white, marked with brown and grey.

The **Purplerumped Sunbird** (*N. zeylonica*) is another common species in the peninsular plains. The male's head, upperparts and breast are mostly metallic green, crimson, and purple, and rump metallic bluish purple. The lower parts are bright yellow. The female is similar to that of the Purple Sunbird but with greyish white chin and throat, and brighter yellow underparts.

A family closely allied to the flowerpeckers and sunbirds is ZOSTEROPIDAE containing the dainty little **White-eye** (*Zosterops palpebrosa*)—PLATE 92—Hindi: *Băboona*. It is a tiny square-tailed greenish yellow and bright yellow bird with a conspicuous white ring round the eyes ('spectacles') and slender, pointed, slightly curved bill. It is met with in small parties and flocks of 5 to 20 birds in trees in gardens and wooded country. Occasionally much larger numbers collect together. They are entirely arboreal birds and spend their time hunting for food amongst the foliage of trees and bushes searching the leaves and buds methodically, clinging in all manner of acrobatic positions, and peering and probing into them for lurking insects and spiders. In addition to this they eat the pulp of ripe fruits and berries, and the nectar of a large variety of blossoms likewise forms an important part of their diet. While probing the flower tubes for this the birds do considerable service in cross-pollination. As they hop or flit among the leaves they constantly utter their feeble jingling or twittering notes. The flocks break up during the nesting season when the male develops a pretty little tinkling song, rather reminiscent of the Verditer Flycatcher of the Himalayas. The song commences almost inaudibly, grows louder and then fades out as it began in 3 or 4 seconds. White-eyes make charming pets, soon becoming tame and confiding and completely inured to captivity. The nest is a tiny cup of fibres neatly bound and plastered with cobwebs—like a miniature oriole's nest—and similarly slung hammock-wise in a forking twig at the extremity of a branch. It is normally built about 2 or 3 metres up in a shrub or small tree. The eggs—2 or 3—are a beautiful unmarked pale blue, sometimes with a cap of deeper blue at the broad end.

The family PLOCEIDAE contains the sparrows and weavers—perhaps the most widely known and recognized birds even by those who do not specially bother themselves about them. The foremost of these is the **House Sparrow** (*Passer domesticus*)—PLATE 93—Hindi: *Gauriyya*, which has now spread itself practically over the entire inhabited globe. The hen differs from the cock (illustrated) in being earthy brown, streaked with blackish and fulvous above, and with whitish underparts. The Sparrow is an unfailing commensal of man in hill and plain alike, whether in a congested noisy city or outlying hamlet or farmstead. When remote areas are opened up and colonized, it is amongst the very first birds to take advantage and adapt itself to the new conditions. In winter the birds collect in large flocks to feed in and around cultivation. Their food consists chiefly of seeds and grain gleaned on the ground, but they also raid ripening crops of wheat and other cereals, and their multitudes often cause serious damage. In villages and towns the sparrow population is largely governed by the presence or absence of horses and cattle from whose droppings they pick out undigested grain. The birds also destroy vegetable and flower buds and are therefore thoroughly unpopular with kitchen gardeners. To counterbalance these ravages, however, they render useful service to agriculture by destroying vast quantities of insect pests, particularly during the time when they have nest-young to feed, since these are raised more or less exclusively on caterpillars and soft-bodied insects, mostly collected in the standing crops. The breeding male has a loud, monotonous, and aggravating 'song' *tsi, tsi, tsi* or *cheer, cheer, cheer* uttered *ad nauseam* as with fluffed out plumage, arched rump, and drooping wings he struts about arrogantly, twitching his partly cocked tail. Large congregations of sparrows collect to roost at night in favourite leafy trees or thorny thickets, and engage in a great deal of noise and bickering before settling down to sleep. The sparrow's nest is a large collection of straw and rubbish stuffed into a hole in a wall or ceiling in a building whether tenanted or not. Its eggs—3 to 5—are pale greenish white, marked with various shades of brown.

The **Baya Weaver Bird** (*Ploceus philippinus*)—PLATE 94—Hindi: *Baya*, is best known for its remarkable woven retort-shaped nests hanging from trees in the neighbourhood of cultivation. The male in breeding plumage is shown in the plate. The female, and male in non-breeding dress are indistinguishable from each other, both being very like the hen House Sparrow, but with a thicker bill, and shorter tail. Bayas keep in flocks, sometimes of enormous size, in open country around cultivation. They raid ripening cereal crops and are sometimes responsible for very serious local damage. They migrate a good deal locally, their movements depending largely on the monsoon and on cultivation, especially of paddy. Vast numbers gather to roost in reedbeds and sugarcane fields at night, often sharing these with House Sparrows and Mynas. Their normal call notes are a sparrow-like *chit-chit-chit*. In the breeding season the males follow these up by a long-drawn joyous musical *chee-ee* sung in chorus while weaving and clinging to their nests, accompanied by excited wing-flapping to attract the prospecting females visiting the nest colony. The breeding habits of this and our other weaver birds are unique. The male builds a number of successive nests in the same colony which are taken over by females one by one when half ready, and completed by him only if so accepted. In this way each cock may often have two to five nests and as many wives and families all at more or less the same time. The nest is a swinging retort-shaped structure with a long vertical entrance tube, compactly woven out of fine strips torn out of paddy leaves or rough-edged grasses. They are suspended in clusters from twigs of babool and suchlike trees, or palm fronds, usually over water. Blobs of mud, collected when wet, are stuck inside the dome near the egg chamber, whose purpose is not understood. The eggs—2 to 4—are pure white.

Two other weaver birds, common but less widely distributed, are the **Striated** (*P. manyar*) and the **Blackthroated** (*P. benghalensis*). They are most easily differentiated by the seasonal breeding plumage of the males. In the former the breast is fulvous, boldly streaked with black, and the crown of the head bright yellow. In the Blackthroated weaver the crown is brilliant golden yellow and the throat white, separated from the whitish underparts by a prominent black breast band. The woven nests of both are built among grass and reeds growing in water or swamps.

The **Red Munia** (*Estrilda amandava*)—PLATE 95(4)—Hindi: *Lāl* or *Lāl mūnia* is smaller than a sparrow. The illustration shows the male in breeding dress. In non-breeding plumage the male and female are alike: brownish, sparsely spotted with white and with only the bill and rump crimson. The tail is rounded, not pointed as in the Spotted Munia. It is a typical munia in habits and behaviour, keeping in flocks in tall flowering grass and reeds usually in damp localities such as the margin of a jheel. It lives on grass-seeds and insects. Breeding males utter a low continuous twittering song. The lāl is a popular cage bird and more often seen as such than in a wild state. Its nest is a globular structure of grass with a side entrance, lined with finer grasses and feathers and built low down in a bush. Four to seven pure white eggs form the normal clutch.

The **Spotted Munia** (*Lonchura punctulata*)—PLATE 95(3)—Hindi: *Tēliā mūniā* or *Sinēwāz* is of about the same size but has a pointed tail. In non-breeding and immature plumages both sexes are more or less plain brown. The Spotted Munia goes about in flocks, sometimes of over 200 or more, keeping in the neighbourhood of cultivation. The birds hop about on the ground gleaning grass-seeds, and occasionally take winged termites as they emerge from rain sodden ground. When disturbed the birds fly up into trees uttering feeble chirrups. The flock flies in a close-packed undulating rabble as is characteristic of the munias. The nest is globular like the Red Munia's, with the side entrance usually extended into a short tube. It is placed in low bushes, but occasionally high up in the head or on the leaves of a palmyra palm 10 to 15 metres up. The normal clutch is of 4 to 8 pure white eggs.

The family FRINGILLIDAE (Finches) stands very close to the sparrows. It contains mostly bright coloured sparrow-like birds, a typical example being the **Common Indian** or **Hodgson's Rosefinch** (*Carpodacus erythrinus*)—PLATE 96—Hindi: *Tūti* or *Lāl tūti*, which is a winter visitor to the Indian subcontinent. The male has a beautiful rose-pink head, breast, back and shoulders; the female is brown with an olive tinge. In both sexes the heavy, conical finch bill, the distinctly forked tail, and a pale double bar on the wing are conspicuous features. Before leaving their winter quarters on the approach of summer the males assume a more intensely red colour unmasked by the wearing away or abrasion of the paler feather edges of the fresh plumage in which they arrived in autumn. The Rosefinch keeps in small flocks of 10 to 20 birds on the outskirts of cultivation, feeding in shrubbery and standing crops. Its food consists of flower buds as well as berries (such as lantana), banyan and peepal figs, bamboo seeds when available, and ripening jowar, linseed, bajra and other crops. Flowering trees and shrubs such as Sēmăl (*Salmalia*) and Pāngra (*Erythrina*) are regularly visited for the nectar of their blossoms. In the process of reaching the liquid the birds' forehead and throat feathers get dusted with pollen and they doubtless play an important part in cross-pollinating the flowers. The ordinary call note of the Rosefinch is a musical, whistling, interrogative *tooee*? or *chooee*? constantly uttered as the birds move about. Just before they leave for their breeding grounds the beginnings of the loud pleasant song of the male may sometimes be heard. The species breeds in Kashmir and

the western Himalayas at moderate elevations. The nest is a cup
of grass lined with fine roots and hair. It is placed in wild rose or
similar thorny bushes 1 or 2 metres above the ground. The eggs—3
or 4—are blue in colour, spotted and speckled with blackish and
light red.

The last family of the order Passeriformes is EMBERIZIDAE
(Buntings). Buntings are superficially very finch-like, but on the
whole with slenderer, more elongated bodies and longer tails.
Many of them like the pipits, have a great deal of white in the
outer tail feathers which is conspicuous in flight. The best known
among this group are the **Blackheaded Bunting** (*Emberiza melanocephala*) and the **Redheaded Bunting** (*E. bruniceps*)—PLATE 97—
—Hindi: *Găndăm* (for both) of which the males are illustrated.
Both these species are slightly larger than a sparrow, and winter
visitors to our area. The female of the black-headed species is
fulvous-brown above; that of the Redheaded Bunting ashy brown.
The lower plumage in both is fulvous, strongly washed with yellow.
They are seen in the cold season in large flocks, often of both species
mixed, keeping to open cultivation interspersed with bush and
babool jungle. The birds descend in 'clouds' to feed upon ripening
crops of jowar, wheat, bajra and other cereals and often cause
considerable damage. Their depredations do not cease with the
cutting of the fields but continue on the harvested stacks until
the grain is threshed and removed. The masses of glistening yellow
birds against the dark green foliage of the surrounding babool trees
look like brilliant flowers in the distance and present a charming
spectacle. Whilst in their winter quarters with us the only sounds
these buntings utter are a sparrow-like but musical, rather plaintive,
tweet as they fly about. The Blackheaded Bunting breeds beyond
our borders, in western Asia and eastern Europe. The nearest place
where the Redheaded species does so is Baluchistan (West Pakistan).
It builds a cup-shaped nest of weed-stems and fibres, lined with
goats' hair. It is well concealed in shrubbery up to about 1½ metres
from the ground. The normal clutch is of 5 eggs—pale greenish
white, speckled and spotted with dark brown, lavender, and grey.

8

INDIA—THE LAND AND PEOPLE

BOOKS UNDER PREPARATION

AGRICULTURE

1. FOOD CROPS — Dr. M. S. Swaminathan,
   Director,
   I.A.R.I., New Delhi.

2. FRUITS — Prof. Ranjit Singh,
   Horticulture Division,
   I.A.R.I., New Delhi.

3. VEGETABLES — Dr. B. Choudhury,
   Professor of Horticulture,
   Horticulture Division,
   I.A.R.I., New Delhi.

4. CROP PESTS — Dr. S. Pradhan,
   Head of the Division of Entomology,
   I.A.R.I., New Delhi.

5. PLANT DISEASES — Dr. R. S. Mathur,
   Plant Pathologist of Govt. of U.P.

ARCHAEOLOGY

6. THE STORY OF INDIAN
   ARCHAEOLOGY — Dr. Y. D. Sharma, Superintendent,
   Department of Archaeology, Agra.

BOTANY

7. MEDICINAL PLANTS — Dr. S. K. Jain, Economic Botanist,
   Botanical Survey of India, Calcutta.

8. COMMON INDIAN FERNS — Dr. S. C. Verma, Department of Botany,
   Panjab University.

CULTURE

9. TEMPLES OF INDIA — Shri K. R. Srinivasan,
   Deputy Director-General,
   Archaeological Survey of India,
   and
   Shri Krishna Deva,
   Archaeological Survey of India.

10. MUSIC — Thakur Jaideva Singh,
    Formerly Chief Producer (Music),
    A.I.R., New Delhi.

11. DANCE — Shri Mohan Khokar,
Special Officer (Dance),
Sangeet Natak Akademi, New Delhi.

12. INDIAN DRESS — Dr. Moti Chandra, Director, Prince
of Wales Museum of Western India,
Bombay.

13. INDIAN PAINTINGS — — do —

14. INDIAN COINS — Dr. Parmeshwari Lal Gupta,
Patna Museum, Patna.

15. URDU LITERATURE — Shri Gopi Nath Aman, Chairman,
Public Relations Committee,
Delhi Administration, Delhi.

GEOGRAPHY

16. ATLAS OF INDIA — Dr. S. P. Chatterjee,
Director, National Atlas Organisation,
Calcutta.

17. PHYSICAL GEOGRAPHY OF INDIA — Prof. C. S. Pitchamuthu,
Head of the Department of Geology,
Bangalore University, Bangalore-1.

18. GEOGRAPHY OF HIMALAYAS — Dr. R. L. Singh, Prof. and Head of the
Dept. of Geography, Banaras Hindu
University, Varanasi-5.

19. GEOGRAPHY OF ANDHRA PRADESH — Dr. Shah Manzoor Alam, Director,
Hyderabad Metropolitan Research
Project, Osmania University.

20. GEOGRAPHY OF BIHAR — Dr. P. Dayal, Department of Geography,
Patna University, Patna.

21. GEOGRAPHY OF DELHI — Dr. M. P. Thakore,
Head of the Dept. of Geography,
K. M. College, University of Delhi.

22. GEOGRAPHY OF GUJARAT — Dr. K. R. Dikshit,
Dept. of Geography,
University of Poona.

23. GEOGRAPHY OF MADRAS — Dr. (Miss) A. R. Irawathy, Principal,
Queen Mary's College, Madras.

24. GEOGRAPHY OF MADHYA PRADESH — Dr. K. N. Varma,
Prof. and Head of the Dept. of Geography,
Govt. T.R.S. College, Rewa.

25. GEOGRAPHY OF MAHARASHTRA   Dr. C. D. Deshpande,
Director of Education,
Government of Maharashtra, Poona-1.

26. GEOGRAPHY OF MYSORE   Dr. L. S. Bhat, Professor,
Indian Statistical Institute,
New Delhi.

27. GEOGRAPHY OF ASSAM   Dr. H. P. Das,
Professor and Head of the Geography
Dept., Gauhati University, Gauhati.

28. GEOGRAPHY OF ORISSA   Shri M. M. Hasan,
Reader and Head of the Dept. of
Geography, Ravenshaw College, Cuttack.

29. GEOGRAPHY OF THE PUNJAB   Dr. O. P. Bharadwaj,
Principal, Rajindra Govt. College,
Bhatinda, Punjab.

30. GEOGRAPHY OF WEST BENGAL   Prof. S. C. Bose,
Department of Geography,
University of Gorakhpur, U.P.

31. GEOGRAPHY OF UTTAR PRADESH   Dr. A. R. Tiwari
Head of the Department of Geography,
St. John's College, Agra.

32. INDIA—A GENERAL SURVEY   Dr. George Kuriyan
Dept. of Geography,
University of Madras.

GEOLOGY

33. GEOLOGY OF INDIA   Dr. A. K. Dey,
Senior Specialist (Mineral Resources),
Planning Commission, New Delhi.

SOCIOLOGY AND SOCIAL SCIENCES

34. DEMOCRACY IN INDIA   Prof. V. K. N. Menon,
Trivandrum.

35. THE STORY OF INDIA'S LANGUAGES   (Gen. Ed.) Dr. S. M. Katre, Director,
Deccan College Post Graduate and
Research Institute, Poona-6.

ZOOLOGY

36. INSECTS   Dr. A. P. Kapur, Deputy Director,
Zoological Survey of India, Calcutta,
and
Shri K. S. Pradhan,
Superintending Zoologist,
Zoological Survey of India, Calcutta.

37. MAMMALS OF INDIA   Dr. B. Biswas, Superintending Zoologist,
Zoological Survey of India, Calcutta,
and
Shri H. Khajuria,
Superintending Zoologist,
Zoological Survey of India, Calcutta.

(*Note: Other assignments are being negotiated with eminent authors.*)

ECONOMIC GEOGRAPHY OF INDIA

by PROF. V. S. GANANATHAN

The book gives in an objective way the main economic trends of the country including production and distribution. Profusely illustrated with maps and charts.

Demy 8vo. $(5\frac{1}{2}'' \times 8'')$ approx. 150 pages.

POPULATION

by DR. S. N. AGARWALA

Deals with the problems and growth of population in India. There are nine diagrams.

Demy 8vo. $(5\frac{1}{2}'' \times 8'')$ approx. 156 pages.

NICOBAR ISLANDS

by SHRI KAUSHAL KUMAR MATHUR

The author has given an account of the geographical, socio-economical and cultural aspects of the islands. Profusely illustrated.

Demy 8vo. $(5\frac{1}{2}'' \times 8'')$ approx. 260 pages.